science, not art

ten scientists' diaries

science, not art
ten scientists' diaries

edited by *Jon Turney*

photographs by *Hugo Glendinning*

CALOUSTE GULBENKIAN FOUNDATION

Published by the
Calouste Gulbenkian Foundation
United Kingdom Branch
98 Portland Place
London WIB IET
Tel: 020 7908 7604
Email: info@gulbenkian.org.uk
Website: www.gulbenkian.org.uk

ISBN 0 903319 98 5

British Library Cataloguing-in-Publication Data
A catalogue record for this book is available from the British Library

Designed by Helen Swansbourne
Printed by Expression Printers Ltd, IP23 8HH

Cover images: Details from *Inside the Mega-Amp Spherical Tokamak, UKAEA,* digital
inkjet print by Wenyon & Gamble, 2002. © 2002, Wenyon & Gamble, no unauthorised
reproduc￼ allowed. Susan Gamble and Michael Wenyon were Artists in Residence at
the Unit￼ Kingdom Atomic Energy Authority and the Rutherford Appleton Laboratory,
supported by the Regional Arts Lottery Fund, the Vale of the White Horse and the Calouste
Gulbenkian Foundation.

contents

foreword

Science, not Art is a peculiar title which partly reflects the fact that this book has been produced by a Foundation well-known for its pioneering work in the arts. The volume is a companion to *Art, not Chance: Nine artists' diaries,* published in 2001. That title derives from a beautifully succinct quotation from Alexander Pope's 1711 *Essay on Criticism,* which may be well applied to all artistic processes:

True ease in writing comes from art, not chance
As those move easiest who have learned to dance.

The diaries in *Art, not Chance* were written by leading artists (a sculptor, performance artist, poet, playwright, novelist, theatre director, choreographer, composer and musician) and were commissioned in order to demonstrate that art is not the consequence of a lightning-streak visit from some baleful muse, nor the product of a warm and wonderful process called 'creativity', but comes from pursuing an original, almost arbitrary, idea to its limits and working very hard against almost insurmountable odds to realise it in the form of a finished piece of work. The book was well received in the national press – 'generous and radical, with so much passion, angst and imagination seething between its covers ... compulsory reading for anyone who cares about contemporary culture,' said Louisa Buck in *The Art Newspaper*. At the launch, which was held at the Royal Institution, Oxford Professor of Chemistry Peter Atkins was so impressed he immediately made a case for a similar volume of scientists' diaries.

The Gulbenkian Foundation has actually had quite a lot of involvement with science over the past six years, running a grant programme The Arts and Science to encourage artists to engage with new thinking and practice in science and technology, and publishing what has been described as a seminal book, *Strange and Charmed: Science and the contemporary visual arts.* The

Foundation has participated in many activities in Britain and worldwide which support artists working with science, and occasionally vice versa. Despite our increasing interest and our acquaintance with a number of well-known scientists and well-written popular science books, however, it is often hard to imagine what scientists do on a day-to-day basis. The idea of asking a group of them to keep personal diaries began to seem rather attractive. We knew we couldn't present a comprehensive range of everything that goes under the name of science but a small selection might prove very interesting.

The science world, as these diaries clearly show, is almost brutally competitive and those on their way up are often obsessively occupied at their laboratory benches, computers, conferences or field trips. Only when they have made it to the top have they the time to be spokespeople for science in general. We wanted to avoid the elder-statesman stereotype and to find scientists from a younger generation who, though high-flyers, had perhaps emerged from less conventional educational backgrounds and were working at the coalface now. Of those we eventually chose, some were already known to us because they had become involved in the arts and others were located through the Royal Society, which recommended some of its Research Fellows. We all met and discussed the idea, then our scientists went back to their frenetic lives and somehow managed to find the time to keep notes as they went along.

The result is an extraordinarily frank and sometimes poignant collection of personal narratives. Our scientists are clearly brilliant people engaged in tasks which almost defy understanding, yet each lives with an ever-present fear of failure. The same is certainly true for artists but, while they may dread the cruel review, they are responsible to themselves alone and are judged, above all, for their uniqueness. Scientists have to be original thinkers but they are answerable to others every step of the way. A surprising amount of their time is spent writing – applications for grants, papers for peer review and, hopefully, publication – and then worrying about it. Yet more time is spent working as hands-on engineers and technicians, adjusting the sophisticated equipment which plays an essential part in contemporary science. And while they may focus on fine detail at a minute scale in their own disciplines, they also need to find time to keep up with the wider scientific world – no train-spotters these.

We hope *Science, not Art* is as successful as *Art, not Chance*. As Paul Allen the editor of that volume wrote at the time, the artists are 'enquiring, adventurous, as interested in the telling detail as the grand design, self-mocking, problem-solving, inventive, diverse, thoughtful, ambitious, open-minded, sexy, fun.' So are our scientists here. But the purpose of this book is not to encourage readers to make footling comparisons between art and science – a tiresome occupation and not much use to anyone. It is so that we may all, perhaps artists especially, gain some insight into the working world of people who inhabit a different culture but who are engaged in subjects which may have profound implications for the future of all humankind – the mechanism of ageing, the fight against disease, the fragile environment, the nature of the universe. These matters are at the heart of our concerns in the arts as well and it is fascinating and instructive to learn about them from quite different perspectives.

I am extremely grateful to the ten scientists for setting aside time in incredibly busy working lives to keep diaries which are eloquent, honest and wholly unpretentious. Much gratitude also goes to the diaries' editor, Jon Turney, for his quiet efficiency and great good sense, and to Hugo Glendinning for his photographs, which, as ever, are suffused with personality and wit. Thanks also to our Head of Publications, Felicity Luard, her assistant Louisa Hooper, designer Helen Swansbourne, copy editor Jane Barry and publicist Sallie Robins. Warm wishes must go to Aosaf Afzal at the Royal Society, which gives this book its blessing and which, we hope, will find it useful in elucidating the practice of science to the public at large and in attracting adventurous young people to its fascinations.

Siân Ede
Arts Director

introduction

Most people nowadays agree that science is important. But it is surprisingly hard to say what scientists actually do. Why? Well, most of the work takes place in the regulated space of the laboratory, which is a special kind of private retreat (Mary Shelley got that right with her vision of Victor Frankenstein behind closed doors). Even if admission is granted, the esoteric routines of most labs make little sense to the casual visitor. Just as our increasingly miniaturised and integrated technologies are labelled 'no user-serviceable parts inside', so the business of the lab tends to revolve around inscrutable machines taking readings of otherwise invisible phenomena.

If the procedures seem mysterious, it can be equally hard to get an idea of what it *feels* like to do this work every day. What is the ratio of inspiration to perspiration, delight to drudgery? What are the rewards and penalties of really trying to understand a piece of the natural world? How would we ever know? This kind of thing is rigorously excluded from professional scientific journals, with their carefully coded protocols and rational reconstructions of results. Education is not much help, either. The UK's National Curriculum, in which science exists mainly in textbooks punctuated by occasional demonstrations, leaves a distinct impression of science moving from unanswered questions to unquestioned answers. And the process of science as it appears in the media is at least as much of a caricature as the process of police work as depicted in *The Bill* or *NYPD Blue*.

Of course, there is a literature about scientific work. Sociologists and science writers who have spent time in the lab have provided revealing accounts of scientific practice. For this volume, however, we have done something different, asking the scientists themselves to set down how it was for them. We persuaded ten exceptionally interesting young researchers based in Britain to keep six-month diaries, relating what happened in their lives from day to day, week to week. There were few preconceptions about what they would tell us. We imagined there would be at least as much frustration as fulfilment. If they spent six months of tedium failing to get an experiment to run properly, that should go in. If trying to make sense of a mass of data felt like knocking against a brick wall, that was fine too. We expected that most of them would make some kind of narrative out of their daily jottings but did not insist on it. All we really asked for was honesty. Not, of course, complete frankness – there is no reference here to the colleagues people cannot abide, the incompetents they may encounter among the bureaucrats, or the dubious publication standards of others in the field. So we make no claim that the diaries reveal the whole truth. But they should offer more truth about working science than is usually told.

So what did we find out? Perhaps the first thing was that scientific practice today is extraordinarily diverse – another reason why it may be hard to say what scientists do. Any one researcher seems to do a great many different things, often at the same time. There are experiments to design, students to see, papers and proposals to write, colleagues to meet, presentations to make. And somehow there must be thinking time amid the constant round of emails and engagements.

And the science which gets done is wildly multifarious, too. Here, it includes plotting the likely behaviour of pairs of black holes as they interact, dissecting creatures brought up from the ocean bed, modelling the behaviour of DNA as it untwists before it can be copied, trying to estimate whether the biomass of a rainforest is increasing and by how much, diagnosing the cause of death of the owner of a skeleton several thousand years old, and unravelling the genetic peculiarities which can extend the lifespan of nematode worms two- or threefold. Some of these things are done on expensive field trips, some under the lab microscope, some while switching between pencil and paper and computer runs.

But although the questions which preoccupy them are so different, our ten do have things in common. One is their dependence on special instruments to return information from the bits of the universe they are looking at, whether very large or very small. Some things, like a skeleton, can be inspected with the naked eye, but most investigations gather information about things which are far larger or smaller, faster or slower, than we can normally perceive. It sometimes seems there is hardly anything scientifically interesting still to be gleaned through the unaided human senses. Putting the right extra-sensory aids in place and getting them to work is a major preoccupation. Computers are part of this, of course – the mathematicians may still work mainly through manipulating symbols by hand, but even here computers are making inroads. But the other aids to observation are varied, although all, again, are potential sources of frustration. Whether hitching a ride on a miniature submarine to sample the ocean depths, building a new kind of spectrometer to pin down the way electrons behave in exotic molecules, or trying to get sensors which measure the carbon dioxide uptake of trees to work in a mangrove swamp, scientists rely on other people's technologies built into their machines. As these are mostly machines which work to their limits, they go wrong much of the time and our scientists have to try and understand why. Even something as simple as looking down a microscope trying to see the right cells can be wearying. It confirms the recollection of Sir Paul Nurse, now a Nobel laureate, about his days as a graduate student, who 'found the drudgery of real experiments and the slowness of progress a complete shock'.

Allied to a preoccupation with the instruments is an obsession no one could miss – money. There is no getting round this. Scientists live the life of the mind, certainly, but they do so in a materially very complex world. Almost all depend on extensive support networks and on costly equipment. Even the theoretical cosmologist in our group is part of a team trying to get $20 million from the US National Science Foundation for a large programme of astronomical observations. From this top end of the scale down to funding a post-doctoral assistant for another few months or raising the fare for a visit to another lab, the equation is simple. No money: no data. And the competition for the money is intense, as almost all the diaries show. Like encounters with instruments, many grant applications end in failure.

In fact, failure or the fear of failure is here a theme in itself. There are so many ways to fail – grant refusal, not getting the experiment to work, not understanding the data, failing to persuade anyone else of the importance of what you have found. One gets a sense that doing new science is an extraordinarily exposed way of life, an activity where mutual criticism is compulsory. Present your peers with a startling new result or a brilliant theoretical novelty and they may admire it. But they will also feel duty-bound to try and tear it apart. Only if it survives this mauling does real credit accrue to the discoverer.

So this is a risky profession, in the sense the biologist Mark Ptashne once related to historian Horace Judson. Asked why he had succeeded in isolating a then elusive molecule in the cell known as the repressor, Ptashne replied that most of the other people who claimed to be on the track of the repressor were not willing to take the kind of risks necessary to do the job. 'What kind of risks were those?' he was asked. 'Well', Ptashne said, '*psychic* risks.'

There are psychic risks aplenty here: risks in applying for grants, making presentations, submitting papers to journals, enduring comments from the referees to whom scientific journals send papers before they can be published. Above, all, there is the risk of simply not understanding and either being defeated by the obscurity of some natural phenomenon or being exposed as inadequate before one's colleagues. There is no doubt that this is an unusually talented and privileged group of people. But who feels talented or privileged from day to day?

You need a strong personality to overcome the fear of failure which is bound to haunt anyone trying to discover something new. Fortunately, it is also clear that what renews motivation is that the experience of making a discovery – even a small one – is as good as it is cracked up to be. For all the frustrations and pressures, the quest is clearly addictive. There is pleasure when experiments go well, satisfaction in giving a good talk, even occasional jubilation when a grant application is approved. But nothing compares with that moment when you know you have glimpsed something hitherto unseen by anyone. This may also explain why they all work so hard.

Our ten diarists give the reader an idea of what it is like to do science in Britain and internationally today. How representative are their stories? They cover a wide range of disciplines but there are many others which remain unrepresented. They are all based in universities but lots of scientists work in other settings – doing research in industrial labs or in dedicated institutes, working on regulatory science or weapons systems rather than academic questions. Some of these scientists might paint a different picture. Our ten nearly all have reasonable security of tenure and a good deal of autonomy while still being able to spend some or all of their time actually doing research (just how much time is a constant worry for those who also teach). Ask ten younger scientists scrambling for short-term appointments as PhD students or post-docs, or ten older ones trying to postpone becoming full-time administrators and committee members, and the image would be different again.

Still, for those lucky enough to be at this stage with the experience of some success while still hungry for more, old enough perhaps to enjoy a little wheeling and dealing without losing sight of the original point of it all, it seems a peculiarly rewarding enterprise. Fragile in some ways, complex and frustrating certainly, but ultimately worthwhile.

So next time you read some popular news report which drops in that well-worn phrase 'scientists have discovered that...' perhaps you will have a better sense of how they arrived at their findings. I think of the evidence here as an extended reply to the small boy who was once quizzed in the education gallery of a well-known museum. Here was a display of oddities, strange samples and unfamiliar objects. How would scientists find out what one of them was? Easy, said the boy, they would look the answer up on their computers. Happily, there is a bit more to it than that.

Jon Turney

JON TURNEY is Senior Lecturer in Science Communication in the Department of Science and Technology Studies, University College London. His books include *Frankenstein's Footsteps: Science, genetics and popular culture* (1998), which won the BMA Prize for popular medical book of the year, *A Quark for Mister Mark: 101 poems about science* (2000), which he co-edited with Maurice Riordan, and *Lovelock and Gaia: Signs of life* (2003). He regularly writes and reviews popular science for *The Guardian*, *The Independent*, *New Scientist* and the *New York Times*.

cosmologist

Janna Levin

JANNA LEVIN, at the time of writing, was an Advanced Fellow in the Department of Applied Mathematics and Theoretical Physics at the University of Cambridge and living in East London with her musician husband, Warren. She is currently at the University of Oxford with a fellowship from the National Endowment for Science, Technology and the Arts (NESTA), splitting her time between the Department of Astrophysics and the Ruskin School of Drawing and Fine Art. In 2004 she takes up an assistant professorship in her native USA at Barnard College of Columbia University, New York.

She began academic life in philosophy but was so impressed with the profound influence of scientific ideas on philosophical questions that she took a double major in astronomy and physics at Columbia. She has a PhD in theoretical physics from MIT and has held research posts at the Canadian Institute for Theoretical Astrophysics and at UC Berkeley before coming to the UK in 1998.

A theoretician, Janna Levin's research interests include the shape and extent of the universe and its large-scale structure. She specialises in investigating new areas of mathematics and exploring their possible application to cosmological problems. As her popular science book, *How the Universe got its Spots,* relates, she is intensely interested in whether it can be shown if the universe really is infinite in extent – she wonders if it isn't. Infinity is a beautiful and profound concept in mathematics but an impossibility in the physical world, in her view. Her diary relates the launch of the book, her involvement with a team of observational and experimental physicists in submitting a major grant proposal in the USA, and a serious professional disagreement about an aspect of the behaviour of the astronomical objects known as black hole binaries.

Saturday and Sunday 1–2 December 2001, San Francisco
All in all a hellish trip to the west coast, culminating in sudden psychotic rants

from my cab driver who has followed me up the abandoned hill and, when I turn around to raise my unimpressive fists, merely waves the strap which has fallen off my luggage. He suddenly wears an air of great politeness, as though he hasn't just been screaming that my 'vibes are all wrong'. I find the keys to the sublet, procured over the internet, hidden in a small combination box behind a gate, a bush and the dark. When I finally make it up the steps, the many many steps, the night-time view is glorious – an unwitting collaboration of millions of individual lights flicking on and off, somehow randomly organising into the collective splendour of this luminous city among the lumps of earth, bay and bridges. Eventually I sleep. I wake. I eat a burrito. I surprise some friends. I go to a grant meeting.

The grant is for a new Cosmology Center that will span several universities and experiments with its core at Berkeley. The principal investigators on the grant wonder why I make the sacrifice of showing up for this meeting. No one wants to write grants. I hate writing my own grants. But I come here for the macho stories. They've hooked up a videoconference between Berkeley and the observatory in Hawaii and we giggle like children when the webcam goes awry and persistently focuses on the back of the director's head. During these technical delays the guys tell me about their last trip to the ice (that is, the South Pole). I particularly like stories about the ice. These guys build things, telescopes and instruments. They launch rockets out of the earth's

atmosphere, burrow deep into the ground or smash things together in colossal accelerators. All in an effort to record signals from the cosmos that our eyes aren't able to catch. There's a toughness and confidence about them that amazes me, but mostly in a good way.

One guy on our team takes astronomical observations from the South Pole where the air is so cold that it sits still and thin and lets more light from space hit the ice without distortion. Fifteen minutes is the most a human can tolerate out on the ice before freezing to death. And they risk these fifteen minutes to check on hardware and troubleshoot experimental equipment. When the planes drop off at the pole they don't come back for months and when they do they leave their engines running so the fuel doesn't freeze. Another guy builds telescopes that are sent up in high-altitude balloons to get a clearer look at the light left over from the big bang. The payloads have been known to land in remote parts of the Andes where they become the idols of local peoples – mistaken for tokens from the gods because they have dropped from the skies. It must be a terrible let-down when scientists from North America come to claim the remains.

This time we're asking for around 20 million dollars from the National Science Foundation and I feel these people are good company to have in such a brazen request. We ask for no more than the other applicants. Last year I went with them to Washington to make a pitch for nearly 20 million. Our grant wasn't approved which, needless to say, was disappointing, so Berkeley is making another bid this year. Was it politics last year or didn't we deserve it? Hard to tell. We were close.

Today the director says we're scrapping the theory section from the last proposal and he expects even Janna will agree. Agree with what? I'm caught off-guard. What am I nodding to? That the last theory proposal was crap? Why single me out? I didn't write it. Or did I? I did write it actually. If I think about it I basically wrote it. I had to compile something out of the shards from other theorists. So am I a hero for stepping in where no other theorist dared to tread or am I a leper, the one who wrote the crap proposal that wasn't funded? In the end four of us will go to Washington to represent our proposed Center.

As I'm just a theorist, I mostly work alone or sometimes with one or two other people. My tools are primarily pen and paper. Feeling integrated into a team is sheer novelty for me. My work just barely edges into the realm of the observable. Lately my focus has been on chaos and black holes and, before then, infinity and topology and, before that, some quantum effects. George Smoot, the well-known experimental cosmologist, tells me there are string theorists to integrate into our theory program in the grant proposal but I should lobby for some more quantum gravity. So that's the sort of thing I'll aim to do.

Monday 3 December
Making progress with black hole binaries. Feels strange and slightly intimidating to work on something with such immediate observational relevance. Using some mildly abstract theoretical machinery involving fractal sets and numerical simulations, I can show that two black holes can orbit each other chaotically. A slight change and the entire orbital history would alter too, in a way that we couldn't manage to predict. In our own galaxy there may be many of these pairs. They absorb light and emit none, so they are sitting completely dark against a dark sky, invisible to our telescopes. Two orbiting black holes generate changing warps in spacetime that emanate as waves from their swirling centres. These gravitational waves travel through the universe and wash past us on earth, squeezing us slightly, stretching us slightly. Imperceptibly. But we're building ambitious experiments here on earth and in space that aim to detect these waves and finally see black holes directly.

There is no small bit of resentment from some members of the astronomical community that I might be jeopardising the funding for their experiments. Their fear is that their current experimental plan will fail to see chaotic orbits. I personally believe their experiments can succeed regardless, but only if we are prepared for what's out there – including chaos. I make clear my unfaltering support for their experiments but re-emphasise that this does not make the chaos go away. We will have to deal with its likely effects in the gravitational wave experiments. I feel disappointed by this particularly political turn of events.

Wednesday 5 December
The new grant recruits ask about last year's Washington trip, as though any sliver of espionage might help us this year. This is what I remember: we arrived in Washington and drove straight to the National Science Foundation. After identities were confirmed and badges assigned and hallways flowed from in front of us to behind us with many corners turned, we reached the double doors between the grants panel and us. We tensed as we catwalked single file into a room of 30 laptops with some people behind them. The panellists with more than one laptop looked like DJs. I expected them to start spinning with a loose, cool angle to their hands, but of course they didn't. They leaned back and looked very very tired. The panel had had to endure two solid days of these presentations. Five groups make it to this stage and each of the five has four constituents, each with a presentation, usually one theorist and three experimentalists. On the first day we used polished slides and well-rehearsed arguments, with an absurdly long pointer for the occasional emphasis to plead, implore and convince. Then that night they slapped us with questions and criticism and by morning the next day we did our best to defend our aims.

After the interviews we tried to accumulate calories at a loud suburban food chain for a few stolen minutes before going back to reformulate our attack. Inevitably we bumped into the members of competing groups doing the same. Everyone knows each other and friends were more aloof than is natural. That day we were competitors over 20 million dollars, years of sustainable research and the future of our universities and scientific aspirations. Just for that day we didn't chat so freely. We tried to read the gait of the other groups. Was that a confident swagger? We conjectured about the strengths and weaknesses of what must be in their proposals. I have always recoiled from particularly competitive atmospheres and I was fascinated to see that in this instance it was not vicious or ugly. Just cautious.

We got to the hotel and within minutes unpacked our gadgets, hooked up cables, printers, modems, phones, computers. I felt like a spy. A false sense of importance tingled me for a second, quickly followed by the almost audible swish of a sense of inadequacy.

Months of preparation, weeks of writing, days of performing – and our grant was turned down. Comments from the panel: we had been generously funded in the past, maybe this wasn't our year, time to spread the money around, try again next year. That sort of thing. So here we are again this year giving it another shot. This time I'm just hanging back to watch how the projects and aims have changed. These are early months and I will be back in London by the time the Washington call comes.

Monday 10 December, New York City
On my way to visit my new publisher, Princeton University Press. Am overwhelmed on return to a New York that I haven't seen since September 10th 2001 when I left the World Trade site. This was my city but I don't recognise myself in these crowds anymore. There is a characteristic space between people in New York, a way they occupy the air and glide past, avert their eyes, check their watches, brush their hair, and it is these fleeting motions that used to make me feel I belonged to the throngs of varied millions here. But I've been in London for years now, and time and distance have wedged themselves between my urban love and me. I don't care about those pretty shoes in the window on 8th Street. I don't care about those newly designed dinners and cocktails or vanilla Stoli with club soda and lime, Max Fish, Luna Lounge and Ludlow Street. Well, I care about those places a little. I'm standing in a photo from my past, watching it shift with me inside, moving slowly, but this is a dulled memory and it leaves me despondent.

I look down the avenues as I cross New York from west to east and gape at the empty horizon. I try to act natural and not stare rudely at the city's scars.

I visit Jaron Lanier, the inventor of virtual reality, in his loft within debris' reach of Ground Zero. Inside, his space is a musical instrument-laden refuge from the burnt smell outside. There must be 2,000 instruments here, things I've never even heard of from countries whose names I don't easily recognise. We have a great talk about fundamental physics, the edges of mathematics and chaos, all of our mutual friends. We plan to meet again in another part of the world.

I take the number 1 train until it rises above ground into Harlem and rumbles my friend's building. From inside her room it feels as though the brickwork is being battered by a mounting storm.

Saturday 15 December, London

Still reeling from an upsetting letter from another research group in another department. Employing a more conventional method than the fractal basin method I've used, they're attacking my recently published article on black holes and chaos. They claim to prove that there is no chaos. They have a written paper which states that I am just completely mistaken. Panic descends. How could I have made such an error? I check. I recheck. I calculate. I code. I compare, cross-check, test, think, freak out, calm down, check some more. Sleepless nights. I find no error. My results hold up. I talk to Neil Cornish, my sometime collaborator. He's going to run an independent check of my calculations.

I believe this work is sound. But if I have made a mistake, it'll be a very severe blow. Publishing an error is a real kick in the stomach for any theorist but it has to happen from time to time. Even Albert E. made mistakes, or so I reassure myself. But my anxieties won't be pacified and have bloomed lusciously by the end of each day.

Thursday 10 January 2002

Still Neil finds no error in my results. He confirms the presence of chaos. We have to return to the methods outlined in the other group's paper and see what's happening. We have already made much progress along these lines.

Wednesday 6 February

Official publication day for *How the Universe Got its Spots: Diary of a finite time in a finite space.* I wait all day for a courier to deliver the first bound copy I've seen. I wait energetically, with zeal. I call my editor three times to tell him it isn't here yet. It is officially early evening when the package arrives. I rip it open and immediately feel too anxious to look between the covers. What if there's a typo in the first line or half the pages are missing or I want to do a radical edit? I put it on the shelf and sit as far away from it as possible.

7.00 am

Phone interview with BBC London Radio. I lie on the couch under ratty covers with a sore throat making itself known. In the dark with my eyes closed I have my five minutes with an unfamiliar voice on the other end then crawl back in bed where Warren mumbles quietly, 'That was great babe.' (I make a mental note to listen to more radio.) My throat hurts. I can barely talk. I think I have strep throat.

2.00 pm

Interview with a reporter from *The Times*. I like her and we chat easily, despite seized throat.

4.00 pm

Reporter and photographer leave. My voice is completely gone. I start to whimper with surely uncharacteristic self-pity. Some kind of punishment for my earlier lack of sympathy for sore throats – particularly Warren's. My neighbours Whitney and Ben give me sea-salts to dissolve in warm water and gargle. We all take a cab to the Royal Institution. I try not to talk and feel like an imposter diva. We pick up Warren on the way and he makes us all laugh with stories of his worthless position in life as a barman in a failing bar. Even the driver chimes in.

6.30 pm

At the Royal Institution. My first book-signing. Adrenalin starts and I try to ignore my rapidly dividing streptococci. I find the signing embarrassing. Don't know what to write inside the books. I remember a tennis star from the 70s once marked a napkin for me with the words 'Stay sweet babe'.

7.30 pm

Give a lecture. I project throughout the talk as though the vocal pipes are in ideal working order. Amazing, the anaesthetising effects of adrenalin.

9.00 pm

Dinner with Baroness Greenfield, Director of the Royal Institution. The RI guest list includes Sir Roger Penrose (excellent) and Lord and Lady people I don't yet know and Peter Tallack, my editor, most fun. My mom says, 'I assume the Baroness doesn't cook.' I eat like a bird because of impossibly raw throat, giving gravely false impression of my eating habits. I'm afraid to tell the guests of my ailment, lest I should appear contagious – which I probably am.

11.00 pm

Get home in tears, in part from hurting throat, in part from feeling sorry for myself. Real reason – probably exhaustion.

Thursday 7 February

7.30 am

Car arrives to take me to BBC Broadcasting House. Do radio show *In Our Time* with Melvyn Bragg, Astronomer Royal Sir Martin Rees and theorist Julian Barbour. I love live radio, though in retrospect I giggle too much. Must not do that in future.

10.00 am

Car to Heathrow, long lines, catch flight to New York for faculty interview at Columbia even though I know in my bones they have no intention of hiring me, and if they did it would mean a big change from life as a researcher. Arrive half dead. Sleep.

Friday 8 February, New York City

10.00 am

The games begin. Half-hour meetings with every faculty member, student and passing stranger who might be keen to deliver judgement. Inspection lasts for two days solid. Somehow I don't mind. Taking lozenges like mad. Bring salts and stock up on a range of products. No time for doctor.

4.00 pm

Give my job talk. Worst talk I've given in ages. Don't know what happened. Missed the mark entirely. Feel dejected.

5.30 pm

More meetings with faculty. See some of my favourite professors who deliver lots of gruff and wonderful words of support. Fever. Sickness.

Saturday 9 February

The same interview procedure all over again. They can't get enough of the candidates. If I can feel this badly and interview, I can feel this badly and have fun. Saturday night out with girlfriends and go crazy downtown. Drink Martinis and act outrageous. Will pay for it tomorrow.

Sunday 10 February

So sick I don't leave hotel room.

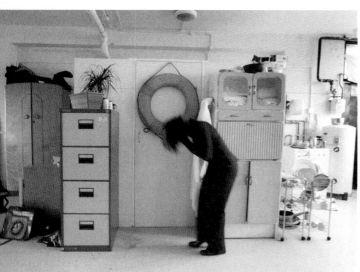

Monday 11 February
12.00 noon
My sickness has finally subsided but doctors advise me to go on antibiotics to avoid terrible and painful death from rheumatic fever. I comply.

7.30 pm
Fly back to London feeling deflated. Have slight onset of claustrophobia behind leaning seat, open tray and pile of airplane rubbish. Want to flail around. Technical problem on plane. Nearly two-hour delay.

8.30 pm
Pilot announces something really frightening about O-rings and fuel tanks. Isn't that what caused the *Challenger* disaster? Another hour's delay.

Thursday and Friday 14–15 February, London
For the next few days I'm here at the Wellcome Trust to act as a juror on their Sciart Award scheme. We'll have long, full days of interviews and tough decisions. Who to fund? What are our aims? Do we emphasise art at the expense of science? Science at the expense of art? Will any of these projects really come to fruition? Now I'm on the other side of a grant table making decisions that will inevitably be resented by some. The best part of these few days is the remarkable company I get to keep with the other jurors and organisers of the Awards. The long hours in a heartless room over, a few of us

jam into cabs to attend the Artangel opening of artist Atom Egoyan's work *Steenbeck*. After a couple of glasses of art-opening wine I queue up for the overcrowded but definitely interesting exhibit. Make a plan to return later to give the work a better viewing.

Wednesday 20 February
On my way to be interviewed by journalist at *New Scientist*. Pass Borders and check to see if my book is in yet. Still not there. I look under new non-fiction. Maybe it'll be in a different section...

Friday 1 March
Get updates from Berkeley team on the status of the grant application. What they have pulled together is impressive but merit alone won't secure the funding. I daydream about how great it would be to have a new Cosmology and Gravitation Center flourishing there again. They've been invited to the final round of interviews. Fingers crossed.

Thursday 4 April
For months Neil and I have been reworking the other group's test for chaos. We apply four independent methods and even when we use their test we confirm chaos in the black hole orbits. We think we can locate the error in their reasoning. Feeling slightly better if a bit furious about the damage this year has done. We write up our results to prepare them for publication. The

tide feels as if it's turning. Except for the days when it feels like I'm hanging off the edge of a cliff by my crooked finger joints trying to hoist myself above the ledge, and just as I glimpse salvation I find a foot poised waiting to kick me back down.

Wednesday 1 May
Big, sad disappointment. I hear from the Berkeley team that the grant has been declined. Brutal news. The proposal was excellent. The team was excellent. The amount of work and sheer time that went into the building of the proposal was colossal. I don't know how it could have been noticeably improved. But this is how it goes, time and time again. You get some grants but not most. I imagine how depleted the team must feel.

Monday 1 July
Invited to a Cambridge college lunch. A Fellow of the Royal Society explains to me that said institution recently came under some criticism for being sexist. Which is entirely untrue, he assures me. I have no cause to doubt him. I personally have always had very good experiences with the Royal Society. 'The real problem', he says, 'is that the women aren't any good.' I sputter and laugh over my limp salad. When I recover my table manners I quip, 'We're not racist, it's just those damn black people.' But he doesn't find me funny. I keep fuming, chuckling, whimpering. I don't want to have this conversation anymore or ever again. And I keep thinking this to myself like a mantra. I don't want to have this conversation anymore or ever again. I reinstate my vow of silence on the feminist issue.

Tuesday 2 July
Finally, finally, finally Neil and I have submitted our papers. Vindication. I'm too drained to be enthused. Just relieved and that feels plenty good in and of itself. I send the other group conciliatory notes. They are not happy. I don't think I've heard the last from them.

ecologist and meteorologist
Yadvinder Malhi

YADVINDER MALHI has been a Royal Society University Research Fellow in the School of Geosciences, University of Edinburgh, since 1999. He read natural sciences at Cambridge, specialising in physics, and took a doctorate in meteorology at Reading. A brief stint on the science journal *Nature* was followed by his move to Edinburgh in 1995.

His research interests focus on how tropical ecosystems are responding to global climate change. Will trees grow faster and absorb some of the extra carbon dioxide humans are generating, for example, and how will this affect biodiversity? Investigating this takes him most often to South America – mainly Peru, Brazil, Bolivia and Ecuador. He is particularly interested in combining a range of observations – including micrometeorology, traditional forestry methodology, satellite remote sensing and global atmospheric measurements – to build up a detailed picture of the exchanges between the forests and the atmosphere.

His diary moves between two field trips and the pressures of life back home, not least those of getting married.

Sunday 6 January 2002, flying to California
The first big trip of the year and I am numbed by a long flight, lost baggage, a missed connection and an enforced overnight stay in Houston. I'm on my way to a workshop on climate change in tropical cloud forests. The other workshop participants are North and South American scientists from a variety of fields, with expertise encompassing botany, ecology, climate and weather modelling, prehistoric pollen analysis and satellite image analysis. Until now most of my work has been on the lowland tropical rainforests, particularly Amazonia. This meeting offers the exciting prospect of shifting attention to new types of ecosystem. The special feature of cloud forests, which grow at

high altitudes in mountainous regions, is that the plants get much of their water directly from condensation from the clouds. The flight provides a chance to read up on them.

Wednesday 9 January, Santa Barbara
We are planning research for the next few years and today all our ideas begin to come together. The most exciting moment is a presentation of satellite images of the southern Andes, and people speak up, sharing their in-field experience of different areas. Suddenly our proposed study becomes real and as we scan images of vast, remote forests and spectacular mountains, our adrenalin levels rise. We finally select a study site: the 'Inca Wall' near Cuzco, Peru, where the Andes tower up from lowland Amazon rainforest. This is where we will tackle the question of what will happen to cloud forests. For the next hour I stand up and begin to flesh out with everyone the details of what we will measure and how and where. Nobody has any funding for this work yet but we return to our offices with semi-crystallised plans, warm relations with new collaborators, and the inspiration to apply for the money.

Sunday 13 January, Arizona
A short flight to Phoenix, Arizona, to visit a colleague who is spending six months working at Biosphere II (Biosphere I is the 'real' global biosphere, the

Earth). This is an amazing place. Perched on a mountain in the Sonora desert, it was developed ten years ago by a Texan billionaire to be a perfectly self-enclosed ecosystem. Within the giant greenhouse structure, there is a sealed-off rainforest area, an ocean with coral reefs and a beach, a mangrove swamp, a savanna and a desert. For a few years a team of ten 'bionauts' tried to live inside, totally cut off from the outside world. It wasn't viable – ecosystem science is still too complex and poorly understood – so five years ago it was redesignated as an ecosystem research station to examine the effects of climate change.

Originally my visit was intended as an opportunistic peek but it turns out that the scientists here are keen to build research contacts with people working with real ecosystems. After a two-hour tour of the structure, we are ushered into a formal meeting. We describe our research interests and plans and, to my delight, we negotiate a salary for my research student Emiliano for one year's work on an experiment on artificial drought in the rainforest.

Tuesday 15 January, Quito, Ecuador
Straight from red Arizona desert to green Ecuador. A blazing morning with the equatorial sun shooting up towards the zenith. I sit on the hostel balcony, looking out over a ramshackle street, a mishmash of colonial-style houses and concrete blocks. To my left the forest-clad slopes of a volcano tower above the city. Over recent years we have amassed evidence that even the remotest and most pristine forests are being altered by atmospheric change and we are looking for the clinching data. We locate plots in undisturbed forests that

were sampled 10–20 years ago and re-measure tree biomass, tree species composition and soil and leaf properties. This Ecuador expedition explores some of the wettest forests of Amazonia, nested up against the Andes where the humid trade winds slam into the wall of mountains and, like a squeezed sponge, shed their water as torrential rain.

The expedition will last for six weeks but I am here for only a week – to ensure that this expedition fits in with the wider pan-Amazonian design. And I also have the self-appointed task of ensuring that the right relationships develop with the right people in Ecuador in order to steer the initial planning decisions.

Wednesday 16 January
A bright blue Quito morning as we get ready for our road trip into the Amazon Basin. The team packs at sunrise in a mood of sleepy-eyed excitement. The journey is stunning. First we plunge off the side of Quito into a deep valley, then climb up to the continental divide. The high pass, at a breathless altitude of 4,000 metres, is ringed by snow-capped volcano-gods – Cotopaxi, Antisuyu, Cayembe – and covered in the bizarre grasslands of the paramo ecosystem. We descend through cloud forest into dry valleys partially deforested by settlement and up again into the clouds through the next range of foothills. This is the first barrier encountered by the rain-laden air of the Amazon and there is a noticeable change in humidity. The cloud forest stretches out over the apparently endless cloud-decked ridges of the Andes. In front, lowland Amazonia beckons, an almost unbroken expanse of wild forest continuing thousands of miles across the continent.

The field station at Jatun Sacha is basic but well-designed. It sits in a relatively small area of protected forest in a region that has been densely settled by Quechua highlanders. We are assigned our jungle cabins – there are ten of us, from Ecuador, Colombia, Brazil, Peru, Germany and the UK. We eat dinner, drink cachaça (Brazilian sugar cane rum), laugh, talk about plans for the morning and longer-term ideas. Now, while the others are asleep, I sit and write these notes amidst the flickering shadow-dance of the moths. The forest is full of insect song. Orion blazes overhead in the pitch-black sky.

Thursday 17 January
In the morning we mark out old forest plots in a floodplain and a dry-land forest, delighting in seeing armadillos, squirrel monkeys, giant millipedes,

ground turkeys. In the afternoon I hike with Pedro, a likeable local Quechua guide, up and down trails to find a remote plot. The forest gradually soaks into my skull and I feel healthier and more centred than I have during the whole British winter. It's hard to explain. Something to do with being part of a world ancient and mysterious and feeling it in your skin and senses, not just in your intellect. I wish that Rachel, my fiancée, were here to share this.

Sunday 20 January

I go home tomorrow but the expedition continues for another five weeks. Despite exhaustion, the field team drags itself out for a farewell drink at a nearby shack-bar. The bar turns out to be closed, but no one minds the effort. We laugh our way home beneath a crescent moon peeking out between the tall silhouettes of the forest trees, the air heavy with the fragrance of white ginger flowers.

Tuesday 22 January, New York

After a week of forest isolation, I connect back into the global mind while changing planes here. The talk is of war: it rumbles on in Afghanistan and may move to Iraq; the Israel–Palestine conflict continues and there is the threat of nuclear war over Kashmir. Much of my wider family lives a few miles from the India–Pakistan border. The big world and its tragedies suddenly overwhelm me. Returning home means facing an enormous back-log of tasks. I have to submit a paper on 'Carbon in the Biosphere and Atmosphere in the 21st Century' to a special issue of *Philosophical Transactions of the Royal Society* by the end of next week. Then there are long-delayed revisions to another paper and two reviews to deal with, all of which should have been finalised months ago.

Wednesday 23 January, London

I stay with my parents overnight and download 300 emails. After the simplicity of the forest, life here just seems so complicated. I feel disoriented and daunted. Funny, after so many years of tropical fieldwork, I can still be hit by culture shock. Flying back to Edinburgh tomorrow.

Tuesday 29 January, Edinburgh

I'm trying to slip back into the rhythms of a normal working week. Lingering jet-lag leaves me groggy in the mornings and awake at midnight. The paper writing requires steady, continuous effort so I am trying to alternate between one hour on this and one on other tasks. In the mornings I am too easily distracted but by mid-afternoon the mental juices are flowing and I am writing well. Still, I realise that I won't finish by the end of the month and so request another week's grace from the editor.

Wednesday 6 February
The carpet of anarchy that had crept across my office over the past month seems to be slowly retreating.

Friday 8 February
I stay in until 8 pm to nail and finally submit the paper. It is later than I planned but it is good to reach the weekend with the satisfaction of a completed task. Looking through it one last time I spot many errors but am quite surprised at how much I like the final manuscript.

Sunday 10 February, London
The days are lengthening and there are the first hints of spring. My wedding draws nearer. I feel very close to Rachel, as we struggle with some difficult decisions. Today is a very significant day. We go to Southall and meet up with my mum and sister to look for an Indian wedding suit. We're staying the night at my aunt and uncle's, the first time that Rachel has met anybody beyond my immediate family. They've taken warmly to her. I haven't been in Southall for ages and enjoy being back in Little Punjab. As I wander through the streets, I can't help wondering how much of Punjab I will be leaving behind, how much I have already left behind and how much ever belonged to me in the first place.

Friday 15 February, Edinburgh
I feel content with the world and bike in early to work. I spend half an hour browsing this week's new issue of *Science* on the web. There are some interesting articles on the effects of volcanoes on climate and why biodiversity is higher in the tropics, but my eye is also caught by some articles on the emergence of art in Africa 70,000 years ago, much earlier than previously supposed, and another on ecosystems around deep-ocean volcanic vents. Reading across this breadth of subject matter invigorates me. It makes me feel part of a bigger, global enterprise: the human discovery of what this universe is all about.

Sunday 17 February

A fun weekend with Rachel. A mixture of theatre, parties, swimming and running in the bright sunshine, doing various household tasks and sending off wedding invitations. As the wedding approaches, I feel more prepared to enjoy it.

Saturday 23 February

It takes a few weeks after returning from fieldwork before people realise that I am back and more emails start flooding in, with little tasks that need to be done and requests for help. When there are so many things to do, one of the main challenges is to maintain a common thread that gives me a sense of achievement and progress. Otherwise I just feel as if I'm treading water. What have been the major activities this week?

1. Revising a paper that describes the rationale and goals of our forest expeditions. I need to put in more on the uncertainties and the methodologies. I have invited my friend and colleague Jim to work up part of this analysis and it's been fun sharing my office with him for a couple of days.

2. Preparing a contribution to a private US initiative to set up 50 long-term monitoring stations in tropical ecosystems worldwide. I really have no time to do this, but the potential is immense. We could be influential in deciding what gets measured in these tropical forests and then be involved in analysing the data coming in from them for years to come.

3. Our students from Brazil are emailing me with problems that have arisen in the analysis of some data. Helping them make sense of it always requires careful thought.

4. The Ecuador team has returned from the field. The expedition was largely a success (they managed to sample seven sites in one of the most fertile regions of the Amazon, an invaluable addition to our dataset) and I feel proud of them. Another post-doc, Simon, has sent in a brief report from his fieldwork in Nigeria. His trip sounds difficult, even epic. The challenge in Nigeria is finding forest plots that have not been logged over. So much of West Africa's forest has been trashed.

5. On Wednesday I give a lecture on global change to final-year undergraduates. I don't do this often but enjoy their intelligent questions.

I've also felt inclined to do a bit of wide-ranging exploratory reading this week, about life as information processing, about information theory, about whether plants show intelligent behaviour and about the bizarre life found on ocean vents deep within the earth or at the bottom of Antarctic lakes. I'm not sure whether this will help me in any obvious way in my own work but I feel my subconscious is burrowing away at an idea. Can the theory of information help us understand biodiversity?

Thursday 28 February
So many things to do. I wonder if I upset people by not replying to all the emails I receive? Not replying regularly every day is the only strategy I can use in order to leave some space for creative thinking.

Sunday 3 March, Budapest
I'm at a conference for the European project that funds our work. After the conference dinner I work on preparing my presentation. Rather than recycling old Powerpoint slides, I decide to work up all the recent data from our expeditions to Peru, Bolivia and Ecuador. I reckon it will only take an hour but as the graphs begin to appear before my eyes, I become increasingly fascinated. At site after site, the same results emerge. In mature forests tree growth should be roughly balanced by tree death, with no net increase. Our data shows that almost every forest plot is increasing in biomass. This is what we've been looking for but I am amazed to see such a clear signal. It is a moment of discovery. Intrigued, I work until 4 am, which guarantees that I will be bleary-eyed for the morning sessions. But it's worth it.

Tuesday 2 April, Edinburgh
Tim sends the biomass results from the recent Ecuador expedition. Again, every plot we've measured shows an increase in biomass over the past five years. It is astonishing that we find the same pattern almost everywhere we go. I still can't quite believe it.

Wednesday 3 April
We have a paper published today in *Ecological Applications*. It analyses the uncertainties in measuring the sizes of tropical trees and how this affects our estimates about how much carbon is being absorbed by tropical forests. About seventeen months ago we made a heroic effort writing this paper. But by the time it is published I am so busy with other things there is hardly a moment to celebrate. The paper passes into the world unheralded. It is only over the years as people read it and respond to it – or not – that its significance will be judged.

Friday 5 April
At work until 10 pm. My student Barbara is writing up her PhD thesis while working in a new job in Rome. She is finding it a lonely struggle and in my busyness I have been negligent in sending comments back on her draft chapters. She has sent a blunt email this morning and I feel a pang of guilt.

Wednesday 10 April, London
The day of the legal wedding. Rachel and I are married and, after all the nerves, it feels beautiful. The ceremony itself is fantastic, warm, intimate. Once you accept that your life has changed, that you live as two not as one, you just soak in the intense new sensation.

Sunday 14 April, Cambridge
So much has happened over the wedding weekend that if I wrote down all the details they would fill a book. There has been music, chaos, dear old friends, relatives from far away, the elegance of Cambridge, memories from India, nervousness, last-minute crises, and love.

Sunday 21 April, Belize
A little honeymoon paradise. But today I need to dip back into work. I must find out if my latest research grant bid has been successful (submitted to the UK Natural Environment Research Council last December). The proposal is to set up a transect of study sites in Bolivia, from wet rainforest to dry forest to savanna, with the aim of understanding how tropical vegetation may respond to possible future drought. A lot hangs on this; the referees' comments have been positive and I am nervously excited.

Right: time to check the email.

Well, now I know. The grading was high enough but we just missed the limit of the money they had available. I feel disappointed, all the more so because it was so close. The saddest thing is that getting this core project would have triggered so much more auxiliary work: a Spanish post-doc working on tropical fires, security for our Brazilian PhD student, links with other groups. All this has to be put on hold and maybe cancelled. The Brazilian PhD may not survive the delay. So much work for no reward.

Wednesday 1 May, Edinburgh
The week is taken up with a three-week backlog of emails, while at the same

time preparing for the field trip to Brazil next week. My feet barely touch the ground.

Friday 3 May, en route to Brazil
Rachel's great-aunt, the former Labour minister Barbara Castle, died today, hours before I was scheduled to leave for Brazil. It has been a difficult decision to go. At the field sites in Brazil researchers have gathered and are relying on me to bring critical equipment and fix broken instrumentation. But my wife needs me to support her in this week of sadness. For once, I go to Brazil with an uneasy heart.

Sunday 5 May
So I am back in Brazil, my most regular research base, for three weeks. We have an ongoing project studying the carbon and water cycles of the rainforest and coastal mangroves, and observing the effects of drought by keeping the rain off a hectare of rainforest with a raised structure of plastic panels. In contrast to the pan-Amazon expeditions, this is hi-tech, equipment-intensive science. The first week will be spent at a remote rainforest in Caxiuanã, with subsequent weeks on an intensive research campaign in the mangroves. We arrive at the Caxiuanã field station by slow river-boat and are met by a speedboat that glides us through the mirror-still waters. The evening sunlight splashes across sky and water. All seems complete. The busy, busy world is disappearing, the forest and sky are slowly seducing me again. I chat with my colleague Patrick about the project, about grant money. Our funds are running out. So much is working beautifully here that to stop it now, just when the scientific returns are flooding in, would be madness. We are overspending our grant in the hope that future funding may bail us out. Not the wisest way to work, but our priority is getting the scientific results.

Tuesday 7 May
This is about my tenth trip to Caxiuanã. Why do I keeping working here? Considering the amount of time I have put in, I have had very few scientific publications in my name associated with the site. I think one major factor is a sense of loyalty and commitment to the dear friends I work with. The other factor is probably just the special beauty of the place.

Friday 10 May, Belém

A day wandering about the city buying items for tomorrow's trip to the mangrove research site. A lot of time is spent looking for someone to make frames for sensors to measure the precision growth of trees. We wander through the sweltering shanty towns of Belém from metalworker to metalworker, until finally we find a steely-eyed man who is able to do the work.

Sunday 12 May, Ajuruteua Beach

For the mangrove campaign all ten of us will be lodged in a shack on an Atlantic beach. This is a nice option in the right season, but today is a windy grey morning of continuous rain. Two of the party struggle in the gale to fill a tank with seawater to measure how much carbon is coming out of it. In the afternoon I potter around with some new sensors, with the aim of using them to measure the daily growth and shrinkage of the mangrove trees to an astonishing 0.001 mm precision. It is one of my happiest ways of spending a day: opening a box with new instruments, learning from scratch how they work, puzzling over manuals, then testing the equipment out on a tree. On each trip I like to try out something new to add a new strand to the fieldwork.

We paddle by canoe along a sea channel to reach our instrument tower, which is about to be flooded by the tide pulled by the new moon. The equipment is broken but not beyond repair. We work until dusk and then paddle back.

Monday 13 May

The last few days have been hard work but satisfying, with a fair dose of both comedy and frustration. Most of all there has been the magic of discovery – of measuring and seeing what we find. There is a chance to get to know the ecosystem, to watch the clouds come and go, the ocean rushing in and flooding the mangrove, the litter of the mangrove washing out and scattering on the beach. The scientific instruments are like extra eyes on the rhythms and processes of nature at work, so that you can see carbon dioxide gushing out of the roots, being sucked in by the leaves, see trees shrinking in the day as water is pulled up to the leaves, see them growing by minuscule fractions of a millimetre every day, see the water trickling up their stems.

Friday 17 May

The team is thinning out. We are all tired, but there is good humour and our spirits are still high. As the moon slips from new to first quarter, the

tides are dying down and the mangroves are no longer flooded by the ocean. I love this connection between the swing of the moon and the cycles of the mangrove – it combines my passions for astronomy and ecology.

There is disappointment when we arrive at our instrument tower. Despite my best attempts last night I did not react soon enough after one of a series of power cuts to stop the carbon dioxide flux equipment from keeling over. I feel frustrated and spend ten minutes in silence at the top of the tower, staring at the horizon, overcoming my disappointment and pondering what to do next.

Tuesday 21 May
Last day in the mangroves and everything is finally working perfectly, with the Zen of the perfect humming tower on a sunny afternoon. Numbers, information, knowledge flow silently from tree and air to wire to datalogger.

Saturday 15 June, Edinburgh
This week is taken up with a visit from Simon and Tim, post-docs on our tropical biomass-change project based in Leeds. They have collated vast amounts of data from the tropical forests and now is the time for synthesis. We have amassed so much evidence to show that undisturbed tropical forests are increasing in biomass and changing in composition. The most likely cause is the global increase in carbon dioxide levels. In addition, we are finding regional variations in the biomass and the structure of forests. All we need to

do now is work out ways of scaling up from our measurements at individual sites in order to understand how whole regions behave, and to see how well our study sites represent the range of climate and soils found in Amazonia. I am still astonished at our results. We concentrate on comparing the field expedition results with climate and soil data to understand how representative they are. We work hard, live off takeaways and beer, catch the World Cup over breakfast and generally exhaust ourselves.

Wednesday 7 August

The big story, the issue that will shape my work over the coming year, is evidence from our trans-Amazon and African expeditions, evidence that indicates with greater certainty that tropical forests are increasing in biomass and both growing and dying faster. There are still uncertainties to deal with but I now believe that we are seeing major alterations in apparently pristine ecosystems that are driven by atmospheric change. The long-term implications for these ecosystems are, as yet, unknown. Over the next six months I will collate papers on this topic from a variety of scientists into a special journal issue and possibly into a book.

What is more, this work has aroused the attention of the major Conservation International project to monitor tropical ecosystem change in 50 sites. We are giving them advice based on our field experience and will perhaps be helping them with the first few plots. It seems that tropical ecosystems will finally get the consistent long-term monitoring that they need in this time of global change.

neurophysiologist
Mark Lythgoe

MARK LYTHGOE is a Lecturer in Radiology and Physics in the Royal College of Surgeons Unit of Biophysics at the Institute of Child Health in London. His entry into science was somewhat circuitous. After failing his A-levels, he trained as a radiographer – then worked as an extrusionist in a plastics factory, as an attack dog trainer in Israel and, following a diploma in nuclear medicine, on board a 'flying doctor' plane as a researcher investigating the prevalence of tuberculosis among the aboriginal population of Australia. There followed some years devoted mainly to climbing in South America, before he returned to the equally perilous academic life with an MSc in behavioural biology and a PhD in biophysics from University College London.

His research focuses on brain pathology, particularly stroke in children and adults. He has also been involved in several science–art collaborations, notably with the film-maker Andrew Kötting. Their film and installation *Mapping Perception* was premiered in 2002. His diary explores the tensions between making exciting new discoveries and finding the time to write them up in a way which will convince other scientists.

Monday 7 January 2002, London

8.55 am

I start the morning with the daily obsessive-compulsive ritual (which invariably permeates the rest of the day) as I climb out of my bed and into my mind. On trial today is an oil-free, dramatically different moisturising lotion from Clinique. Not a double-blind scientific trial, but a Mark Lythgoe does-it-make-me-feel-better kind of trial. I dress in shorts and T-shirt for my cycle alongside the canal from Hackney to the Institute of Child Health near Russell Square. It's a cold grey morning. I'm chatting to myself as I start to pedal, more ranting than chatting, rehearsing the day's agenda. I constantly talk to myself,

sometimes out loud, sometimes inside my head: why would the blood flow to the front of the brain be different from that to the back, mustn't miss the hospital lunch-hour lecture today, must try to talk to Martin (our statistics mentor) about the rate of cell death following a stroke, must dig out some more papers on delayed neuronal death, organise flights for the Hawaii meeting, read CVs for the post-doc interviews, order animals, complete book chapter on 'Biomedical Imaging in Experimental Neuroscience'. Years ago it was just a few words that I grunted out loud, now it's more of an outburst, an outpouring of things to do, things I've forgotten and things I'm going to do. It's punctuated with frequent swearing. It's a biochemical thing. Somehow it helps me to order the day and prepare myself for what I've got to do. There's a lot of self-punishment in all this.

I love going to work though. There is hardly a day that I don't want to go in, when I can't wait to try out some new experiments. I'm hooked on exploration and that's what makes science, like climbing, so addictive. You think of a problem that doesn't have an answer, take your best guess at it, and then design an experiment to test whether you're right. It's similar to the

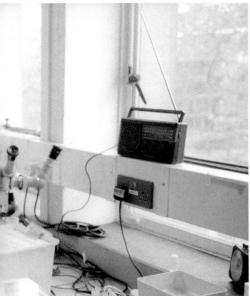

anticipation you feel when you approach a summit, wondering if the view on the other side is how you had imagined it on the way to the top.

Thursday 10 January
3.00 pm
I've just given a brief internal lecture on my research, which aims to understand why brain cells die following stroke, that is, when a small blood clot travels towards the brain and lodges in one of the blood vessels en route, reducing the supply of nutrients, such as oxygen and glucose. Following a stroke, the brain quickly depletes its limited energy reserves. At that cataclysmic moment, a chain reaction starts, an avalanche of biochemical events that must be halted if the brain cells are to survive. Over 20 years ago, two research groups identified a curious type of brain cell death. They demonstrated that a brief period of reduced blood flow to the brain would result in 'delayed cell death'. There is a quiescent period before the cells die. It appeared that the cells carry

a trigger that switches on a fatal cascade, causing them to die several days after the initial event. A similar thing may be seen in babies after a difficult birth.

I can recall the moment about a year ago when I saw a view of the brain on our magnetic resonance imaging scanner that I thought no one had seen before. A small part of the deep grey matter, known as the lateral portion of the striatum, appeared to be more sensitive to a brief reduction in blood supply to the brain (a stroke) than other regions and had started to die prematurely, rather than remaining normal for many hours before beginning to die. Could it be that delayed cell death was not delayed after all? Was this 20-year-old theory wrong? I could feel the hairs rising on the back of my neck. It is in such moments of revelation that all the pain and anguish of research dissolves, when you test your hypothesis and you're right, or you find something you didn't expect and realise its importance.

Today I get to my desk to see that the raw data – the data that possibly refutes this trusted theory – is collecting dusty yellow post-its. So why have I been sitting on them for months? Perhaps because after I've seen the first experiment work, celebrated the novel finding and subsequently repeated the experiment until I'm bored to tears, the adventure is over. The wearisome part is writing it up, manicuring the data into a presentable form for the journal. But not all science can be fun. I must finish analysing the data tomorrow.

Saturday 12 January
Today I'm out of the lab to do some blue-screen filming for *Mapping Perception* with my arts collaborator Andrew Kötting. I cycle from my flat in Hackney to his house in Deptford. The project aims to blur the boundaries between normality and abnormality by taking a look at the world though the eyes of a girl who has part of her brain missing. At the heart of the project is Andrew's daughter, Eden, who has a rare genetic condition known as Joubert syndrome. Today we are filming our version of *Dr Tulp's Anatomy Lesson* by Rembrandt. It's my first day directing.

Tuesday 15 January
David Gadian, my boss, has quite rightly given me an earful about not writing up the Delayed Cell Death data. I will start tomorrow.

Thursday 17 January
Try to face my To Do list and the Delayed Cell Death paper. Once I start on

it I'll be fine. I go down to the lab to avoid it. Today we're trying to find out why our new technique for measuring blood flow in the brain doesn't work. This is a sexy technique, known as arterial spin labelling, which uses a short burst of radio waves to 'knock over' the water molecules in the major arteries in the neck that supply blood to the brain. Subsequently these magnetically labelled water molecules flow into the brain and create a contrast in the magnetic resonance image that is directly related to the amount of blood flowing into the tissue. The advantage of this technique is that you produce images of brain blood flow without injecting dyes into the subject or putting electrodes into the brain. Spend the rest of the day firing pulses of radio waves into the neck and still no image of blood in the brain.

8.30 pm
Must get to the climbing wall before it closes. I need the physical effort to get my life in perspective. Out of all the sports I've tried, I keep going back to climbing. I always feel like a kid waiting for Christmas to arrive before I set off for a day outside. I think it's the same with science. I'm looking for adventure, trying to get a handle on the unknown.

11.00 pm
Back from the wall. Depressed. Trashed my left-hand ring finger on a small crimp attached to the 30-degree overhanging training board, known as 'the woody'. The base of my finger has swollen up and I think I have partially detached one of the pulley ligaments that hold the tendon onto the finger. Well, that's two months off climbing – the only bonus is that I can use the time to clear some work. Some bonus.

Monday 21 January
2.00 pm
A grants meeting at the Institute of Child Health. It's the first time I've been involved with this panel. I get so edgy before these meetings. I'm constantly worried about my ability when surrounded by incredibly bright people. I'm persistently at or beyond the limits of my knowledge. I never used to be like this. Somewhere during my science training I lost a little of Mark Lythgoe. I never realised that I would be so regularly tested, or that my confidence would take such a battering. Today I'm presenting an application for a grant that isn't mine and I must defend it to the panel, which includes the Dean and

Chairman of the Trustees, Leolin Price QC, guided by some external referees' comments. In fact the topic of the application is as far removed from my own field as philosophy is from science. Although I've done loads of reading, I can feel my heart racing already.

4.00 pm

'Fuck, fuck, fuck! Why did I get so tense? It's just a fucking discussion. I can do this.' A few more laps of the toilet on the ground floor. 'You fucking dimwit,' I scream at myself.

4.15 pm

Back in the lab and I feel inconsolable. I don't really know what I've done wrong. No one has said anything, no one has suggested I didn't present well, there's not even been a glare from the Chair or other members. I felt a huge amount of pressure to get it right. But this is only one of the many daily pressures and today it was all a little too much. *(A few days later, I spoke to one of the panel members about it, only to find that my presentation was more than fine. So why the stress?)*

7.00 pm

Still at work, still reflecting on the day's performance at the panel. I'm not sure why I like science so much. It can be a humbling experience. I guess it's in part because I've had some pretty shit jobs in my time before getting my chance to be an academic.

Friday 25 January
3.00 pm

Crack. No pain, just a crack – an olive stone! Phone Ruby my dentist for a quick check-up. I go into the chair with a mouth full of molars and now I'm toothless. I feel as though I'm falling to pieces. Isn't it old people who lose their teeth? Obviously not. Dribble through the musical *Rent* in the evening. I love musicals, but *Rent* could never compare with *West Side Story*.

Friday 1 February

Meeting with a neurologist, Vijeya, from Great Ormond Street Hospital to talk about stroke in children and an unusual conditional called moyamoya syndrome. The children suffer from narrowing of the main arteries in the neck that supply blood to the brain, which leads to a high risk of recurrent stroke and progressive cognitive impairment. In trying to compensate for the lack of blood flow, many tiny vessels grow in the brain. The name moyamoya derives from the Japanese word meaning 'puff of smoke' and describes the appearance of these fine vessels. There is currently only one treatment, an operation that involves attaching one of the blood vessels that supply the face to one of the blood vessels in the brain via a hole drilled through the skull. We are looking for alternative therapies.

10.45 am

Walking back to the department after the meeting I begin to get excited about using a genetically modified virus. Simply, if we remove the components that make the virus infectious, insert a piece of DNA to produce a blood vessel-growing gene, on injection into the brain it may induce new vessel growth and hopefully restore normal blood flow to the brain. My pace has started to quicken. I must get a grant together while my enthusiasm lasts.

11.00 am

Rest of the day in the lab – can't get the virus thing out of my mind. How do we get the virus into the brain? Will it stay there long enough to induce the new vessel growth? Perhaps we can inject it into the ventricles (the fluid-filled sacs in the brain)?

Friday 7 February

David asks about the Delayed paper, as it now seems to be affectionately called. I explain that after a moment of uncontrolled enthusiasm I've advanced the analysis and instead of showing the classical pattern of delayed cell death, the figures seem to confirm a gradual and progressive death over the first ten hours following a very brief stroke. This starts a two-hour discussion on the cellular causes of the changes on the magnetic resonance images. What is it about these dying cells that affects the image? The MRI scanner measures the movement of water in the cells and we wonder if there is an active process in the brain cells that is halted, thus producing a reduction of water movement and a subsequent image change. We hypothesise that if this active process ceases during cell death, the image will alter. It's a difficult theory to test, so we agree that I must trawl the literature to find evidence from other studies to back up our idea.

Monday 11 February

5.40 pm

Set off to hear a talk at the Institute of Physics on 'molecular motors' in the hope that it will patch together our rather flimsy theory. On the way over I'm chatting to myself once more. 'Tomorrow I will look at the data again and try to finish the Delayed paper. I'll start with Martin's "time course analysis".' By this he means look at the raw data, don't immediately average your data then subsequently use the average to describe the whole experiment.

Wednesday 27 February

My morning ritual is interrupted by the post. I open the handwritten letter, 'I write to you with the sad news that Yvonne Tabaillou passed away peacefully at Homerton Hospital on 14 February.' I'm numbed. I've known Yvonne for nearly three years and in that time she massaged my various climbing injuries from knotted bundles of fibrous scar tissue into the fluid form that has kept me climbing. Yvonne gave me the healing that couldn't be applied to her cancer. I miss her cold hands and warm heart already.

Friday 1 March

10.00 am

A rather convoluted phone call from the PR agency Bolton and Quinn who are promoting the *Head On* exhibition at the Science Museum which is about the art and science of the brain. Artist Annie Cattrell and I have made sculptures conceptually based on thought processes – *Hearing and Seeing*. They want to create a press release about whether there are differences between the MRI brain scans of the scientist Richard Gregory and the artist Richard Wentworth. I explain that no conclusion can be drawn from just two brain scans, although the images may be used as a point of discussion. They like the sound of that.

Monday 3 March

7.30 pm

I arrange the brain scans, with the approval of David Gadian, and *The Guardian* comes to report on the discussion with Richard Gregory, Richard Wentworth and the biologist Lewis Wolpert, who is also based at UCL and is interested in everything. I explain that there are differences from the average in the brains of children who have difficulties with maths, or of musicians with perfect pitch.

And London taxi drivers show newly developed differences after they complete The Knowledge. This last finding suggests that our brain can reorganise itself to deal with newly acquired information. Either way, it is possible to imagine that the mind of a mathematician or a physicist may have become different from that of a visual artist or a dancer. (Although there is no scientific evidence to suggest this as yet!)

I wonder if I was born to be an artist or scientist? Last year Professor Simon Baron-Cohen, expert in autism at Cambridge, presented data to show that scientists scored significantly higher on a standard scoring test for autistic tendencies than either humanities scholars or social scientists. Does this mean that certain autistic qualities help us to become scientists? Is that why I ritualise my breakfast or the way I pack my climbing gear? Is that why scientists dress differently from artists? While I am musing, the conversation in the group has turned off science and art and onto something far more important – grants. I rarely hear David talking about such matters. 'The grants system is flawed. Imagine if you were in the consumer industry and you had devised a business plan, let's say for Tesco, covering the next five years. In order to get the proposal approved you are obliged to ask Safeway's CEO to review it! It's unthinkable in the business world, but happens daily within science.'

Monday 11 March
No closer to understanding the information re the MRI changes for the Delayed paper. Spend the afternoon talking to David and statistician Martin to try to come to some sort of agreement on the wording in the paper. We can't come to a consensus on whether there is enough data in the literature to support our hypotheses – that the MRI changes are due to a cessation of an active process. After each discussion it takes days to digest all their comments and it's a tedious process to redraft the paper.

Wednesday 27 March
Martin says that we can't use the word 'gradual' in the paper without more statistics. More delay!

Tuesday 2 April
9.30 am
Someone else's scientific paper sits on the corner of my desk. The abstract concludes that it is '... the first report of [reduction in lesion volume] in cerebral

ischaemic preconditioning' – a subject perilously close to my own field of research. It's an awful reminder of how competitive scientific research is. I can't face reading it. Every time I see it I feel sick. I'm depressed and jealous because I didn't do it myself. I'm not too sure if I was always like this. Just to compound matters another article is dropped on my desk, 'Publish or Perish' by N.R. Barrett.

Wednesday 3 April
The post arrives late today with the referees' comments from the second journal that I'd sent an earlier paper of mine to. I always feel a little sickly as I read the comments. I scan for the beloved words and here they are: 'Your paper has been accepted for publication without corrections.' Thank you. Thank you. Thank you! '... invaluable in stroke research', and further on '...the authors have clearly done enormous work...' This was more than I could wish for. I read on, surely not more praise? '...they report on interesting findings...'

Yet how is this possible? The first journal rejected my paper with the comment that it was the runt of the litter and should have been drowned at birth.

I cruise around the department all day showing off my referees' comments. It's not really a celebration as such, more a blessed relief I don't have to resubmit. In the evening I meet an old friend, Dominic, for a beer in the pub. I keep telling him about my paper and he frowns as I try to explain that there

is a rigorous system by which a paper is accepted into a peer-reviewed journal. 'One thing's for sure,' I say to Dom on the way out of The Rugby, 'peer review like this doesn't happen in the art world: "Dr Hirst, we suggest that in the light of previous work the blue dot (row 3, column 3) should actually be cyan. We look forward to your resubmission in the near future."'

Friday 5 April
10.00 am

Go over to have a chat with Ted who's reading the newspaper and eating his beetroot sandwiches with his feet up on a chair. He's 77 years old and comes in two days a week using his Reliant Robin to get him to the station in South Wales. Ted arrived in our department before the advent of computers (and still uses graph paper to plot his data), after working with Lord Brock on the first heart–lung machine. I find him complaining about his new white surgical wellies. When you see his early papers, featuring heart bypass equipment and buckets of foaming blood, you realise why he's so attached to his footwear. 'What's up Ted?' I call. 'I ordered the same make, same size and they still don't fit,' he replies. Three hours later he's back from the shops with a pair of black gardening wellies. I find him cutting the tops off them to keep them the same height as the old white pair. I holler a few congratulations on his ingenuity. Later that day I'm sitting at my desk and hear him racing off toward the lab to see how his brain-cooling device is going. The flash of his boots never ceases to bring a smile to my face.

Monday 6 May
10.00 am
Epilepsy meeting to discuss the long-term effects on children following a febrile convulsion. Clinical specialist Rod Scott explains his findings that children who have prolonged epileptic seizures may suffer spontaneous recurrent seizures leading to cognitive deficits later in life. We discuss the possibility of applying to the Epilepsy Research Foundation to investigate the effects of recurrent seizures on brain development.

Friday 10 May
Off to Hawaii to present the delayed cell death data at our MRI annual meeting. Back in two weeks. Great job!

Wednesday 29 May, London
Ouch, I'm hobbling around the department today after having my piles injected. What a toe-curling experience. I'm not going to cycle home today.

Thursday 4 July
David asks me to see where we are up to with all the grants as we need to get more money into the department. I constantly worry about money. I want to bring more people in to build up the group, yet if I'm grant-writing then I'm not doing experiments. It's very difficult finding time to do both well. I love the lab work, playing around on the bench, trying to make something work where others have failed. Those skills do not translate easily to grant-writing. I'm stuck at my desk today and I feel I'm missing out.

Monday 15 July
Been away for a few days. I squint at the screen as my email opens, '234 new emails' – not so bad after all! Paperwork sorted, I go to check on the guys. One of the PhD students, Dan, and Ted are on the MRI scanner. The second I ask Dan, 'How's it going?' I can feel that the scanner's transmitter coil is broken and he's none too pleased. I'm too scared to offer advice so sneak out

quietly, hoping the problem will go away. No chance. Two hours later Dan proclaims that the coil is broken and dumps the remaining part on my desk as proof. I ring Martin. Martin's a gem. Not only is he brilliant, but he has the patience to deal with dimwits like me.

11.30 pm

Martin arrives, Ted's sleeping on the floor of the department so he can start his experiment early and I'm finally editing the Delayed Cell Death paper with the new statistical data from Martin. I'm fond of working at night. It's peaceful and as it gets past midnight there is a significant feel to the hour. Martin works with an array of spectacles, soldering irons, and digital and electronic meters until the faulty capacitor is found and replaced. I feel privileged to work with the likes of Martin. Science is very physical sometimes and the late-night experiment is not infrequent. I'm on my way home, can't go by the canal as they lock the gate after dark. I enjoy it when the science gets a little painful.

mathematician
Marcus du Sautoy

MARCUS DU SAUTOY is Professor of Mathematics at the University of Oxford and a Fellow of All Souls College. He has been a Royal Society University Research Fellow since 1995 and will become Tutorial Fellow at Wadham College, Oxford, in 2005 at the end of his research fellowship. His popular mathematics book *The Music of the Primes* is published by Fourth Estate in the UK and HarperCollins in the USA.

His work, as he explains below, focuses on the mathematics of symmetry, in its aspect known as group theory. When he won the prestigious Berwick Prize of the London Mathematical Society the citation said that his work had 'completely transformed the study of zeta functions associated to infinite groups, revealing hidden depths and unexpected applications'. His diary records the latest stages in a ten-year effort to stand up a conjecture he formulated about the properties of these functions.

Tuesday 11 September 2001, London

My PhD student Christopher from Cambridge comes to visit me today. I work mostly from home in a tiny room in our flat in London with a wonderful view over a reservoir. I prefer working from home. An office has an oppressive sense that 'you should be working' and if no ideas are coming I find the environment makes me very conscious of my lack of inspiration. At home I can slip in and out of thinking of maths and doing other things. I often listen to music while my subconscious carries on working. I also get to take my son to and from school most days. My partner is currently working full time so I have the fun of looking after Tomer, who is five. We invariably go to school on our makeshift tandem – my bike with a tag-along attached to the back. Tomer hates everyone pointing at us as we ride through the streets of Stoke Newington but I love the attention.

The exercise before starting work helps get the brain cells buzzing. But today I know that Christopher is coming so I stock up on my one great addiction – espressos. As a famous mathematician once said: 'A mathematician is a machine for turning coffee into theorems.' My PhD students have learnt by now that the best place to have my undivided attention is at my home. However, what Christopher has to show me today would get my attention in the most distracting environment.

I work in an area of mathematics called group theory which tries to under-stand symmetry. What I love, though, is to mix subjects, to make connections, to investigate the crossover between different mathematical disciplines. So I've taken a pair of glasses usually worn by the number theorists and I'm using them to look at the subject of symmetry. The glasses are called a zeta function. The zeta function in number theory was first introduced to try to understand the wild list of prime numbers. Using the zeta function, the German mathematician Riemann discovered that it was possible to see order where before there appeared to be only chaos. The zeta function acts like Alice's looking glass, transforming things magically through its gaze.

Over the last ten years, I've been exploring the idea of using a zeta function to look at wild groups of symmetry rather than chaotic primes. As with words

or sentences, mathematical expressions can sometimes form palindromes, reading the same from left to right as right to left. One of the things which has particularly intrigued me as I gaze through these number-theory glasses is a certain palindromic pattern that I have seen cropping up again and again in all the examples of the zeta functions that have been calculated. The zeta function is built out of equations like

$$a_0 + a_1 X + a_2 X^2 + \ldots + a_n X^n$$

where $a_0, a_1, \ldots, a_n$ are numbers. But these numbers always seem to have the property that if I reverse the order, I get the same sequence of numbers:

$$(a_0, a_1, \ldots, a_n) = (a_n, a_{n-1}, \ldots, a_0).$$

If you take a group of symmetries (or we say simply a 'group') and calculate its zeta function then it seems that the answer will always have this palindromic symmetry (what we technically call a 'functional equation').

I have spent ten years trying to understand why one always gets this palindromic behaviour. I'm not sure whether it really will be there in every example that I might calculate. That is why I want a proof. This is what obsesses the mathematician. Evidence in mathematics can be very misleading. The fact that all the examples calculated to date have this palindromic symmetry doesn't guarantee that the conjecture will not collapse when I calculate the next example.

But knowing that a zeta function has this symmetry would not be so amazing as a result in itself. It's more that it is evidence of some deep and subtle structure at the heart of my subject which I don't yet understand. And it is showing a small bit of its beautiful head by manifesting itself in this functional equation. If I can understand the symmetry I am convinced it will also reveal a huge vista of structure that we are currently too blind to see.

In recent years, though, I have been getting quite pessimistic and concerned that I was seeing the palindromic symmetry only because I chose nice examples to look at. Then last year I cooked up a surprising new group of symmetries which had very unexpected properties. I found I could use this group to produce a counter-example to one of the fundamental conjectures, the Uniformity Conjecture, that was posed in 1988 at the beginning of my specialised subject. Finding this example was one of the most thrilling moments in my mathematical life. I was sitting in the Max Planck Institute in Bonn waiting to phone my wife, Shani, who seemed to be chatting for hours

on the phone. I go to Bonn to work with Fritz, one of the few people in the world who thinks on the same mathematical wavelength as myself. As I waited in my office, this example suddenly flashed into my head. It obviously didn't come out of nowhere. I had spent months immersed in understanding the theoretical framework. But occasionally in your mathematical life you get these real revelatory moments.

Many people have talked about the mathematical creative process. I perceive it as if my mind is playing away for months crashing out chords on a piano in my head. Time after time, things just don't sound good. But then suddenly ideas collide which produce a surprising harmony. It doesn't happen often, but when it does you long to reproduce that excitement.

The new group of symmetries that I created/discovered (many hours of fun debating that divide) that night in Bonn opened up a new tunnel. It took us through to a part of the mathematical world that, although it was familiar, we never knew was connected to group theory. I call it my 'elliptic curve example' because it connected groups of symmetries with special curves in number theory called elliptic curves. These curves were fundamental to the recent celebrated proof of Fermat's Last Theorem.

My elliptic curve example had such unexpected properties that I wondered whether it would also be the first example that would produce a zeta function without the palindromic symmetry. After all, I had used it to destroy the Uniformity Conjecture. Perhaps it was malicious enough to destroy my Palindromic Conjecture. The trouble was that I didn't have the perseverance to see the calculation of the zeta function through to its bitter end. I knew enough about the zeta function of this group to recognise that it would contradict the Uniformity Conjecture. But I would have to calculate the whole thing to know whether or not it had the palindromic symmetry.

Why didn't I finish the job? Part of the reason is that I don't like doing calculations. I love looking for patterns and structure, understanding the theory of why things work the way they do. I'm also quite lazy. I chose mathematics because it's the sort of subject that lets you get a long way with a few well-chosen ideas. I don't work long hours. Once Tomer has finished school at 3.45, I'm ready to pack in work and go off to the park to play football.

Christopher isn't scared to attack this calculation head-on. Today he reveals that he has finally succeeded in completing the calculation. I sit excitedly, looking to see if it has the palindromic symmetry. It almost does. But then Christopher explains that there seems to be one bit missing. Here experience can be helpful. I spot one piece of his equation which relates to the elliptic curve. I know that these elliptic curves have zeta functions with the same sort of symmetry. This, I realise, should contribute the missing piece which will complete the symmetry. But will everything really match up so beautifully? I rush upstairs to find the book with the details of the symmetry of the elliptic curve. When we put in the missing piece, as if by magic, the zeta function still has the palindromic symmetry.

It is a very exciting moment for both of us. I feel real pride in Christopher for his achievement. He feels the elation of that first taste of discovery. That flash of illumination is what he will crave for the rest of his life. But best of all, if my crazy elliptic curve example still has this palindromic symmetry then there is renewed hope that my Palindromic Conjecture might still be true. After ten years of thinking on and off about how to prove it, this new discovery gives me a new passion to understand why this symmetry is there.

Half an hour later, Christopher and I are still riding high on the revelation of the afternoon. Shani phones me from work. She says I should switch on the television. Two aeroplanes have crashed into the twin towers in New York. Christopher and I sit for an hour watching the towers crumble to the ground in front of our eyes. An emotional roller-coaster of a day.

Tuesday 20 November, Glasgow

I've done theatre and mathematics all my life and I've never really connected the two. Theatre is something which I used to run away from mathematics to do. I could be physical and not have to live in an abstract world of the mind devoid of physical and emotional contact. Now I've got myself invited to be a panellist on a workshop dedicated to theatre and mathematics, organised by Suspect Culture at the Tron Theatre. So I'll have to start thinking of connections. I guess you can view mathematics as a kind of esoteric performance art.

Ever since I started my Royal Society Research Fellowship I've dedicated a lot of time to the public understanding of science. Bringing Maths to the Masses. A maths teacher in my comprehensive school, Mr Bailson, took me round the back of the maths block after one lesson where he smoked his break-time cigar. I thought I was in trouble. But he suggested that I might enjoy reading some popular books to find out what mathematics was really about. I was twelve years old. Just the effect of someone taking an interest in me meant that I was intrigued to find out more.

It was a revelation. I had spent my time in the classroom learning the scales and time signatures of mathematics but no one before Mr Bailson had shown me some of the beautiful music that you can play and listen to once you've mastered schoolroom arithmetic. So now I dedicate part of my working life to writing articles for newspapers and talking on radio, in the hope that something I write or say might inspire some twelve-year-old to see that there is real beauty and passion in mathematics. Besides, to have a piece of writing appear within days and read by thousands is a new sort of pleasure. The time-scale for erudite mathematical research articles means that my paper will often be published several years after I've sent it to the journal. And my readership? I'm lucky if 100 people really read and appreciate the intricate line of argument that I've spun to prove some new pattern that I've discovered. It's like writing very modern esoteric music that requires years of musical experience to decode the complexity of its sound.

My time at the moment is split between trying to crack the mystery of my Palindromic Conjecture and writing a popular maths book about our greatest unsolved problem – the Riemann Hypothesis. This book isn't so far from my academic interests. It is all about the zeta function. And I'm getting a reputation for being an intelligible mathematician, which is why I get myself invited along to interesting events like this mathematics and theatre workshop.

The theatre I love doing and watching is physical theatre – very European in style and the kind Peter Brook is so good at creating. Indeed, when you listen to Brook it could be mathematics he is talking about: 'Small means, intense work, rigorous discipline, absolute precision. Also, almost as a condition, they are theatres for an elite.'

The event at the Tron is excellent. As I begin to explore why I love doing theatre and mathematics I see common themes which I've never been aware of before. I love the challenge of using the magical space of the stage to create, for example, the impression of a boat crossing a raging sea without any props but just using actors. The confines of the stage mean that you are pushed in new inventive directions that you would never find if you were allowed all the resources of a film set. Working in the mathematical world can be very similar. The logic of the mathematical landscape means that you are working under huge constraints yet within those constraints you are free to create.

For the session this afternoon I have decided to create my own mathematical theatre exercise. I have printed out the 50 odd numbers from 9,999,901 to 9,999,999 and give each member of the audience their own number. We then produce a human version of an ancient Greek way to find the primes among these numbers, called the sieve of Eratosthenes. Everyone begins by standing up and waving a number in the air. As soon as someone finds their number is divisible by three, say, they sit down, confident that their number is not prime. But then every third person on from this number will also be divisible by three so they can sit down too. By sieving through the numbers like three, five, seven etc., we begin to sort out the primes from the non-primes. When I talk to people afterwards they really loved the exercise. Some people have become very attached to their particular number. Mathematicians often talk about numbers becoming their personal friends. It is strange how by making people into numbers I've animated these numbers in a way I had not anticipated.

Tuesday 1 January 2002, London
A year ago my wife almost died giving birth to a second baby. Shani made it but our baby died. She cannot have children again. We are trying to find other ways of having more children – surrogacy and adoption. But the stress of the

last year is finding an outlet in chest pains late at night when I'm winding down. So I've given up espressos. I also want to see whether I am self-disciplined enough to do without one of my few vices. No more coffee – no more theorems?

Thursday 10 January

I've spent the last few months looking at a theoretical formula I have for the zeta function of a group. If this palindromic symmetry is really there, I should be able to see it in this formula. I keep turning the formula and looking at it in different ways. The formula is like a Rubik's cube. I keep manipulating it, rewriting it. Turning the sides of the cube, I hope that suddenly all the colours will match up to reveal the pattern I am convinced must be there. But nothing gives.

Friday 11 January

I phone Fritz today in Bonn. I've sent Christopher off for two weeks to work with him. Fritz tells me that he thinks they will prove the functional equation next week! I should be happy but I am devastated. This was what *I* wanted to prove. I knew that I might be making a mistake when I explained my ideas to Christopher. I thought I should be altruistic and think of the greater good of the subject. But now I can't bear the fact that it might be proved by someone else. Have I been cast aside so early? I feel like leaping on a plane immediately.

Monday 21 January

Nearly two weeks have passed. Christopher has returned from Germany. I phone him. It seems that their initial optimism was rather unrealistic. I'm back in the game. But they did find an important paper that I had missed, which helps with one bit of the project.

The day is spent preparing lectures for mathematicians in Nottingham – six lectures in two days. A bit harsh. It has been hard getting my head in gear away from the pop book. I've spent a very demoralising few days, as my editor and agent both smashed into the last two chapters that I wrote. I know I have to soak it up and use their helpful comments but I feel as if I've learnt nothing.

This is also the big weekend for our surrogacy. One embryo grew to four cells and was implanted in our surrogate on Saturday. Now we are just waiting to find out if it takes. We go down into the lab to talk to the embryologist. I find it hard to understand how the four cells might grow into a child. This seems like real science. Whether my Palindromic Conjecture is true or not appears utterly insignificant compared with understanding the mysteries of these four cells.

Wednesday and Thursday 23–24 January, Nottingham
Six lectures to give. Well, a bit of a cheat – four and a half lectures. I've got Christopher to do one and we arrive 20 minutes late for my first lecture because I get lost driving round Nottingham. It's wonderful to have such an attentive audience – mostly number theorists to whom I prefer talking because they have an appreciation of the techniques I'm using.

Monday 28 January, London
I'm still trying to work with my theoretical formula. But I'm realising that since the formula also covers zeta functions not connected with groups of symmetries, it might be too general to see the palindromic symmetry I'm after. Sure enough, when I calculate an example which doesn't have its origins in group theory, the palindromic symmetry disappears. It means the Rubik's cube manipulating of this formula won't be enough. I've got to see why the group theory is important. The calculation is partly done waiting in the doctor's surgery. Better than reading old *Hello* magazines.

Saturday 2 February
A devastating weekend. The pregnancy with the surrogate hasn't worked. We knew it probably wouldn't take. Still, to get so far and – nothing.

Monday 18 February
I've spent the last two weeks in bed with suspected pneumonia. The doctor says I am falling to pieces although he finds it quite an interesting challenge to try to deal with somebody with such a contradictory cocktail of disease. When I get delirious, invariably mathematics plays a role in the hallucinations. I spent a night wrestling in my mind with inane properties of the numbers 7 and 27. Completely meaningless. I've recovered a bit and hope to sit in bed thinking about maths since I can't do anything physical. But actually, thinking about mathematics requires a lot of physical strength. I find my body becoming very tense and strained. I wriggle a lot when I think. Eventually I realise that maths is not the answer and I sink back into a Nick Hornby novel.

The enforced rest has brought me to a realisation, though. My functional equation is probably not going to yield to a detailed analysis of my theoretical formula. Since it seems to work only when the equation has come from a group of symmetries, I've got to find an explanation that captures the source of the equation. This is a blow. It means there is no easy solution. I know I've been here before but this time I thought that a better understanding of my formula would crack it. I have to return to a more conceptual idea. Ultimately this will probably bring greater rewards. The trouble is finding the idea! I think the key is to return to a very tiny example. If I can't give an explanation here for the palindromic symmetry then what hope is there for a more general example?

Tuesday 21 February

Christopher comes today. He has very exciting news. He seems to have made some breakthrough on the functional equation. For certain special groups of symmetries which he has been analysing he can see the 'right' way to cut the problem up so that each piece still has the same palindromic symmetry. It is a very positive affirmation that the palindromic symmetry is really there. No jealousy this time about his progress. Still lots left to understand.

Thursday 4 April

Piano arrives. My present to myself for doing my pop maths book. I've actually ended up buying the neighbour's piano. A fantastic palaver as it goes over the garden fence and then up the stairs to our second-floor flat. I am looking forward to punctuating my work with playing the piano. I'm really bad but I love sight-reading through lots of material.

Sunday 7 April

Start our preparation group to see about adopting a child.

Thursday 25 April, Oxford

Today I've spent an hour or so thinking about my conjecture. It almost feels like a luxury. Pondering on a new way to see this palindromic symmetry is a relaxation after the pressure of the past few weeks. I've been working for the last month on the third draft of my book, writing grant proposals, proof-reading papers, writing a film review of *A Beautiful Mind*, setting a general paper for the All Souls Prize Fellowship ('Is football the new religion? Discuss') and writing a rebuttal to a journal to explain that the referee had completely missed the point of our paper.

I'm in Oxford tonight as I write this. A rare moment these days but I need to show my face every now and again. The bell for dinner has just tolled. So I'd better don my tie and gown – the only moment when I look vaguely decent – and go and eat spicy seared tuna and drink fine wines with the other Fellows.

Wednesday 8 May, London
After my review of *A Beautiful Mind* I'm getting a lot of flak from fellow mathematicians for two silly mistakes I made. Certainly I don't mind being told I got something wrong. It's just the arrogant superior manner that mathematicians can have about truth, as if they alone are its custodians. I will have to get used to it. The trouble with mathematics is that it doesn't leave much room for making errors. Of course this is important because we are all building on top of this pyramid. But it makes popularisation hard.

Sunday 2 June, on a train to Italy
A journey. I think well on journeys, especially trains. The breakthrough in my DPhil thesis dawned on me on a train from Reading to Oxford. This journey is longer, taking me to Trento in northern Italy where I am giving a series of technical lectures. I start scribbling in my pad of paper sitting in the station at Seven Sisters. I'm using Christopher's thesis to bounce my thoughts off. Just reading other ideas can pull one sideways so that suddenly a hole emerges through the wall.

I'm beginning to see a way that I could possibly play off the ideas which yielded a palindromic symmetry, proved ten years ago with Alex, my Israeli collaborator. (I came back from that visit with a theorem and a wife.) It is a way to involve something called the Weyl group, which is an object with lots of symmetry. Ten years ago I had used the symmetry in this group to explain the palindromic symmetry in another zeta function. Now I am beginning to see a way perhaps to use two of these Weyl groups in this more complicated setting. It is still a long way from a revelation but it is a new lead. That is what I needed if I wasn't going to throw my hands up and surrender again to the mystery of this problem. Pursuing my hunch will probably have to wait until I have some books with more details. I have the general idea in my head but details are going to make the difference.

Friday 7 June, Trento
My lectures to the graduate students in Trento have come to an end. I've had

to be less ambitious about explaining all that I wanted to. It is one of the frustrating things about our subject. We are constructing such lofty towers that the beautiful intricate details crafted at the pinnacles are visible to only a few. It takes more than a week to help people to climb to the place where they can appreciate them. But I hope they have been excited by the thrust of ideas. I wonder whether composers feel the same. How many people can appreciate exactly how a composer is able to make the hairs on the back of the neck stand on end? But I guess a composer doesn't need the average listener to have that level of musical understanding. I don't think my lectures have the same physical effect on the audience but I hope they feel inspired and transformed by listening. In his opening address to the International Congress of Mathematicians in 1952, Oswald Veblen expressed well this need for us to perform our theorems: 'Mathematics is terribly individual. Any mathematical act, whether of creation or apprehension, takes place in the deepest recesses of the individual mind. Mathematical thoughts must nevertheless be communicated to other individuals and assimilated into the body of general knowledge. Otherwise they can hardly be said to exist.'

Back to London and the chance to follow some of the new leads that my journey inspired – and to return to those deep recesses.

marine biologist

Jon Copley

JON COPLEY is a Teaching Fellow in the School of Ocean and Earth Science at the University of Southampton and Science Co-ordinator for Autosub Under Ice, a programme to study the marine environment beneath floating ice shelves, using a robot submarine. Jon started his scientific career as a zoologist then took Master's and PhD degrees in oceanography in Southampton, returning there in 2000 after a stint working as a science journalist for *New Scientist*.

His main research interest is in the creatures which live around deep ocean vents – sea-floor features found in mid-ocean where the planet's crust is being created and superheated water wells up from below the sea-floor. As his diary relates, if you want to become better acquainted with such organisms, the first problem is getting to where they live.

Thursday 31 January 2002, Southampton

Deep-sea biology involves long periods of tedium punctuated by brief spells of electrifying excitement. With drifts of admin in my in-tray, today spells tedium. Students dropping in for advice provide a welcome interruption. It reminds me of the scene in an Indiana Jones film where the archaeologist hero is under siege from enthusiastic students and anxious administrators. He escapes from his broom cupboard of an office by locking the door and climbing out of the window. Unfortunately mine is on the sixth floor.

One thing I enjoy today is drafting a new lecture course, which will examine the patterns of life in the oceans and the processes that shape them. This is pretty close to my research: I've spent most of my career so far studying animals at deep-sea hydrothermal vents. The patterns of life around these volcanic springs on the ocean floor are governed by the dramatic geology of their surroundings. The vents are scattered along the longest mountain range on

Earth – the mid-ocean ridge – and their inhabitants are nourished by chemicals in hot fluids gushing from spectacular mineral chimneys.

The discovery of deep-sea vents 25 years ago revolutionised ideas about how ecosystems can be supplied with energy. Studying vents is now helping us understand how communities of organisms can be shaped and transformed by a dynamic environment. Of course, there are more accessible systems that I could study – but there are also 65,000 kilometres of mid-ocean ridge out there waiting to be explored, which is enough to last several lifetimes.

Tuesday 5 February
A colleague in the USA emails this afternoon to say that there may be a spare place on a deep-sea biology expedition to the Gulf of Mexico next month: two weeks at sea, using a submersible to collect specimens from the sea-floor. I rattle off a proposal to Craig, the expedition leader, describing the science I would like to do if I were included.

Thursday 7 February
Still waiting to hear about the Gulf of Mexico. Paul, my former PhD supervisor, pops his head round my door a few times to ask whether I have any news. He will be going with a couple of his current PhD students. In the afternoon I get an email from Craig inviting me along. Ten minutes later I have booked the flights on my credit card and rescheduled my lectures. My goal is to collect

samples for an ongoing investigation of how deep-sea animals keep their proteins in shape under pressure. Some fish and crustaceans use a chemical called TMAO (trimethylamine oxide) to do this – the deeper they live, the more TMAO they contain. But we have only just started to examine the relationship between this chemical and the animals' living conditions.

Other researchers have used TMAO to tackle laboratory models of diseases where proteins get bent out of shape, such as Alzheimer's, cystic fibrosis and prion diseases such as scrapie. Whatever other tricks deep-sea animals use to keep their proteins in order might offer further clues towards new medical treatments. So I will look for this chemical in several of the species that we hope to encounter, whose TMAO contents are unknown. If they contain it, then knowing the amount will improve our understanding of how animal life is adapted to the largest habitat on our planet. And any creatures that lack it will spur us to try to discover what they use instead.

Friday 22 February
Two days a week I work on the Autosub Under Ice research programme. This five-year project involves oceanographers, glaciologists, geologists and biologists from eleven institutions across the UK. Its aim is to send Autosub, an autonomous underwater vehicle, beneath the floating ice shelves up to a kilometre thick that cover large areas of ocean. What goes on there is important for predicting the fate of ice shelves in a changing climate and

understanding their influence on ocean circulation. It is high-risk but potentially high-gain science, similar to a space shot. Success depends on the technology. Right now Autosub is being prepared for trials before its first mission beneath ice shelves next year. One of my jobs is to act as liaison between the engineers and the scientists to ensure smooth progress. The head of the technical team and I have one of our regular chats. Before I go to sea I need to prepare an update for the researchers planning to use the vehicle.

Wednesday 27 February
Just before leaving I get an email from Bram, a geologist colleague, with a proposal to survey for new hydrothermal vents on the Mid-Cayman Rise near Cuba. At a depth of 5,000 metres, these would be the deepest and hottest vents on the planet. Whatever species live down there could be very different from those we already know. Bram likens it to Conan Doyle's *Lost World*. If the proposal is successful, the fieldwork would probably take place sometime next year.

28 February, en route to Florida
Taxi to Gatwick and a flight to Orlando with Paul and his PhD students Liz and Kerry. On arrival we head to Harbor Branch Oceanographic Institution in Fort Pierce, where we board the research vessel *Seward Johnson II*, bound for the Gulf of Mexico.

Friday 1 March, Fort Pierce
Loading the ship with equipment from Craig's lab: microscopes, chemicals for preserving specimens and plastic spars, floats and mesh the significance of which eludes us at the time. A shopping trip in the afternoon completes my own inventory, with ziploc bags for the body parts of deep-sea animals and a cooler to transport them back home on dry ice.

The *Johnson Sealink* submersible occupies most of the aft deck, ready to be launched and recovered over the stern. Designed by Edwin Link and paid for by the philanthropist Seward Johnson, the sub can dive to 1,000 metres. A pilot and scientist sit in an acrylic sphere on the front, while another scientist and a technician ride in a separate compartment behind. The sphere offers excellent all-round vision, unlike other, deeper-diving subs, where your view of the abyss is restricted to a tiny porthole through a metal hull.

Sunday 3 March

There are fifteen in our science party – from Florida, Virginia, Pennsylvania, Norway, Iceland and the UK. Everyone has their own agenda. There are those whose work is part of the grant that funded this expedition and those, like me, who are 'piggy-backing'. We agree a protocol for dividing up work and prioritising whatever we collect. As my work does not tread on any toes here, I can use material that no one else wants.

Our destination is one of the most bizarre places found so far in the deep-sea – the Brine Pool. It looks like a lake at the bottom of the ocean, fringed by a dense carpet of mussels. The 'lake' is a layer of water much saltier and more dense than the sea above it, formed where a rock formation called a salt diapir pushes through the seabed. The methane that also seeps through the seabed nourishes bacteria living in the gills of the mussels, and these bacteria in turn provide the animals with energy. This unusual food chain, similar to that found at hydrothermal vents, supports an oasis of life in the otherwise sparsely populated depths.

Craig is after the mussels. On this trip he will use the sub to fill cages with them and attach them to buoys anchored to the sea-floor. These buoys can be signalled to jettison their anchors by ships passing later in the year, popping up to the surface with the cages of mussels in tow. By putting down several buoys and recovering them at different times, Craig's group will be able to track changes in the animals through the year, looking at their reproduction and nutrition.

In the afternoon I help to build a prototype spar buoy. The design is fairly straightforward: a six-foot pole with a plastic flag on top, threaded through a large round float. A weight on one end of the pole should make it float upright when it hits the surface, waving the flag as it bobs around in the swell. A loop of wire suspended from the bottom of the pole should also allow the sub to attach the lines from the mussel cages.

Tuesday 5 March

Following a good run down the east coast of Florida, with dolphins playing on the bow, we've met rougher weather and spent last night sheltering behind Key West. As we are behind schedule we are now taking a short cut across the Gulf instead of hugging the coast. The waves are about 10 to 15 feet high and the wind 30 to 35 knots, which is lively but not too bad, although we seem to be making heavy work of it. With the waves on the starboard bow, the ship is corkscrewing as we slam and shudder across the sea. Every so often water sloshes along the upper deck where I share a cabin with Paul. Dining in these conditions is always entertaining; those whose reflexes are not quick enough chase their plates across the table, while drawers of cutlery shoot open. And ice-cream flavours are apparently dispensed on the whim of an ice-cream god in the freezer, with tubs spilling out at random whenever the door is opened on a roll.

Tuesday night and Wednesday 5–6 March
Few of us get much sleep, as the ship takes a couple of fairly big hits, losing some equipment off the aft deck and knocking out main power. I am woken by the silence and darkness: suddenly there are no engines, no navigation lights outside, not even a hum from the air conditioners – just water slapping against the hull and a distant alarm on the bridge. The crew gets the bow thruster back on line fairly swiftly and turns us into the weather, but the cut-out repeats soon afterwards. It appears there is a short in the electrical system somewhere, which could be a problem: it might be dangerous if the ship were to lose power during launch or recovery of the sub.

I have volunteered to run the MOCNESS (Multiple Opening and Closing Net Sampling System) when we reach the Brine Pool. This is a series of fine-mesh plankton nets several metres long secured to a metal frame that resembles a bedstead. It is towed behind the ship on a wire. Each net is opened and closed individually on command, so the nets can sample whatever is floating at different depths. By trawling through the water above the Brine Pool, we may be able to catch the tiny floating larvae of the animals that live there. To make the most of our time out here, we will operate round the clock, with the sub diving during the day and the MOCNESS running at night.

I ran a similar system in the north-east Atlantic a few years ago, towing it within ten metres of the bottom in water 3,000 metres deep. This meant swinging more than nine kilometres of wire behind the ship to get a good angle, rather like flying a kite in the dark on an incredibly long string. I enjoyed it, as there is almost an art involved: small adjustments to the ship's speed or the amount of wire being towed are eventually transmitted to the nets, making them rise or fall. You have to keep a picture of what is going on in your head, anticipate changes and resist the urge to over-react.

Thursday 7 March

We have arrived over the Brine Pool and the crew have fixed the electrical fault but it is too rough to launch the sub. So in the evening we make the first run with the MOCNESS. Sitting in the cargo container housing the controls, I watch the depth and angle of the nets on a computer monitor, radioing the bridge to change our speed or the winch driver to pay out or haul in wire. My limey accent causes much hilarity over the airwaves. The MOCNESS goes down to 600 metres and comes up slowly, nets opening and closing on the way.

Once winched back on board, the plankton samples from each net need to be concentrated before they can be examined under the microscope or preserved with formalin. A few of us start this in the lab, leaving Liz and Kerry cleaning the nets outside. Then the ship lurches as a big wave washes across the deck, sending water sloshing around the lab door. Those inside exchange wordless glances and rush out on deck to find it swamped, with kit floating about, but Liz and Kerry fortunately still there. They were wearing lifejackets, of course, though Liz has lost her hard hat, which is now circling the Gulf in the darkness. Both are drenched and shaken, as the rail along the side of the deck had been removed to launch and recover the nets. I stay out on deck. Resetting the nets is a three-person job from now on. We finally turn in at 0300h.

From the meagre look of the samples, the nets may have got tangled as they went over the side of the ship, preventing them from opening and closing properly. So these samples may be of limited value, beyond simply describing what is there.

Friday 8 March

From my bunk I can tell that the weather will prevent the sub from being launched this morning. At the moment I am slated to go on the fifth dive, but five dives are looking unlikely.

Those who were not involved in the MOCNESS run are deploying scavenger traps. These large mesh cages will sit on the seabed like giant lobster pots for the next few days. Loading them with smaller mesh bags of rotting fish heads should hopefully tempt deep-sea creatures inside.

Another MOCNESS run in the afternoon and this time the nets behave impeccably; launch is much easier in the daylight and slightly calmer weather. But best of all, there are mussel larvae in the samples from the deeper nets. These tiny offspring pull themselves about under the microscope with a long, tentacle-like tube foot or swim using their velum – an organ for propulsion they only have as larvae, which looks as though they are shaking out a very hairy blanket from their miniature shells.

Morale is boosted by this first result from the expedition. It offers clues to what time of year the adults spawn and answers questions about when the larvae settle as new recruits to the mussel beds.

Saturday 9 March
Woken before dawn by another change in the ship's motion: more rough weather has arrived. Yet another MOCNESS run this morning, but the ship cannot slow to an ideal towing speed in these conditions. The sea calms down, however, while we clean the nets on deck in the afternoon. The sub crew duly emerge to announce that they will dive today.

The sub goes into the water at 1515h with Paul on board and returns at 1830h, laden with samples. There is a rush to transfer specimens from the containers on the front of the sub into buckets of cold water in the wet lab. And then the sorting begins. We tease apart hundreds of mussels wrapped together by oily filamentous bacteria, picking out the bright orange ragworms and pale shrimp living among them. There are also bundles of metre-long tubeworms in curly tubes with flared ends like skinny trumpets.

Once sorted, the specimens are processed. We team up to extract the tubeworms from their tubes – a delicate operation if you want to keep them intact. Craig's PhD student Sandra then squeezes eggs and sperm from the worms, so she can study their fertilisation and development. The worms have bright red blood that another member of our team extracts for analysis. I take some leftover tissue from the worms to test for TMAO back home, along with the abdominal muscle of the shrimp. Next door the mussel team are dissecting out gonads and other organs for their projects. Frenzied activity until 0230h.

Sunday 10 March
The weather is up to its old tricks again. Craig convenes an ominous science meeting at lunchtime: it turns out there is a serious problem with the A-frame that lifts the sub out of the water. He therefore decides, with unanimous support, to curtail the cruise and bank the remaining ship and sub time for future use. Rather than head for the nearest port, however, we will return to the ship's home base at Harbor Branch. At least we had a good haul yesterday and everyone has something they wanted.

Monday 11 March

Up early to help recover the scavenger traps. The first one comes back empty with one net wall missing. Something large may have picked up the trap and tried to make off with it, ripping open the side. But the fish head bait is still in its mesh bag and crawling with smaller scavengers. Dissecting it, I find isopods – cousins of woodlice – burrowing away like maggots. There are also plenty of amphipods, crustaceans that resemble giant fleas.

The second trap is wriggling with a dozen *Bathynomus*, giant isopods over a foot long. These nightmarish creatures look like something from the *Alien* films. Their faces bristle with sharp mandibles, while their armadillo-like carapaces cover scuttling legs and flapping paddles that they use for swimming. Voracious scavengers, they eat almost anything they find on the bottom – the postmortem of one specimen reveals a stomach full of duck tape from the trap. These specimens are also reproductively mature, containing eggs over a centimetre across, which may be a record for a crustacean.

There are also a couple of hagfish and a hake in the trap. I take some muscle samples from each for TMAO analysis. The hagfish are interesting because they belong to an ancient group of fish whose TMAO content we do not know. The hake regularly migrates large distances up and down in the ocean, so its TMAO content may also be revealing. Does it change TMAO content during these migrations, or keep it at the level needed for its maximum depth?

While we work, the A-frame is miraculously repaired, so now we are not returning to Harbor Branch.

Tuesday 12 March

Waiting for a window in the weather to launch the sub, but this delay provides an opportunity to test the prototype spar buoy and modify the design slightly. Another MOCNESS tow in the evening but the record for larvae from the second haul still stands. The winch is also playing up – it keeps cutting out when paying out wire slowly.

Wednesday 13 March

The sea is flat calm today and the sub dives twice. During the morning I finish building the remaining spar buoys in a flurry of sawing and drilling, while others work on the cages and anchors. The sub puts everything in position in the afternoon, ready to be retrieved on future visits. Comparing the species examined on this trip with results from previous expeditions, however, it

appears that many animals at the Brine Pool are reproducing at this time of year. Such a pattern is surprising in a habitat where the food supply does not appear to vary seasonally. Either there are stronger nutritional links with the seasonal world above than people have realised, or perhaps the animals still have the same rhythms as their shallow-dwelling ancestors.

Thursday 14 March
The weather is still calm and the sub goes into the water again this morning – but comes back with a leak in the hydraulics that power its manipulator arm. This cannot be fixed out here, so we are heading for Gulfport, our original final destination. So no dive for me this trip. Rather than my trying to carry them in my luggage, my samples will stay in the freezer and ride the ship back to Harbor Branch, where they can await extradition.

Wednesday 20 March, Southampton
Several newspapers are running stories about an Antarctic ice shelf the size of Somerset breaking up. 'Antarctica sends 500 million billion tonne warning of the effects of global warming' announces a headline in *The Guardian*. But a quick calculation using GCSE physics confirms that for the ice shelf to have such a mass, it would have to be made out of something several times more dense than lead. Five hundred million billion tonnes of ice is actually enough to smother the planet. You never see a headline attributing the works of Chaucer to Jeffrey Archer, yet similar-sized lapses of scientific literacy are

common. This really annoys me. If people are not being reliably informed on the subject of science, how can they form reliable opinions?

The assertion that global warming is to blame is equally shaky. A position statement from the British Antarctic Survey explains that it is premature to draw that conclusion. If only the story were as simple as 'global warming melts polar icecaps'. But it isn't. Although policy-makers understandably want clear answers to environmental questions, nature seldom obliges in providing them. One of the goals of Autosub Under Ice is to cut through some of this confusion.

Friday 5 April, Southampton Water
A stunning sunrise makes me realise how lucky I am not to be sitting behind a desk. This is the last of three fourteen-hour days of fieldwork with the students taking my Coastal and Estuarine Oceanography course. I am spending the morning on the *Ocean Adventure*, a rigid-hulled inflatable boat with a 140-horsepower diesel engine. She can manage 35 knots over calm seas, zipping about to make hydrographic measurements in different places as the tide changes. In the afternoon I transfer to the *Bill Conway*, our research launch, which is at anchor to monitor changes at one spot. I think the class

largely enjoys the experience, with the long hours building a camaraderie of shared hardship.

Monday 15 April

Paying for the Gulf of Mexico trip has dented my bank balance. Although I have a small grant for the TMAO work that could cover it, I have decided to spend that on extra chemicals for the lab instead. So I need to trawl through recent journals for possible news stories for *New Scientist* that might pay the bills. I find an interesting paper that shows how coral reefs are a utopia of free market economics. The magazine commissions a story about it for next week. It feels odd sometimes, brokering other people's science as a commodity like this.

Friday 5 July

My samples from the Gulf of Mexico are still languishing in a freezer in Florida, as neither I nor my contact over there have arranged shipment yet. I've had a mountain of marking at the end of the semester. And somehow I also ended up running interview days for prospective students and planning another new course for next year. Now my priority is to finish a paper that I have been on the verge of submitting but held back, wanting to add further results to strengthen its case.

Not a good decision, as I could probably have got two papers out of the work. But although we are judged on quantity of publications, I wanted to focus on quality. The paper shows how reproduction around deep-sea vents is a patchy affair. Conditions at vents are very heterogeneous, like those in a big city, and whether some animals can afford to reproduce depends on their 'postcode'. There are also hints of a monthly reproductive cycle for one species – a frequency unheard of elsewhere in the deep sea.

I want the paper to be unequivocal, avoiding Mark Twain's definition of science as the wholesale return of conjecture from a trifling investment of fact. But gradually piecing together what is going on and testing your picture against further evidence is part of the challenge of deep-sea biology. If you could instantly understand what was happening with absolute certainty, finding out would no longer be any fun.

palaeopathologist
Charlotte Roberts

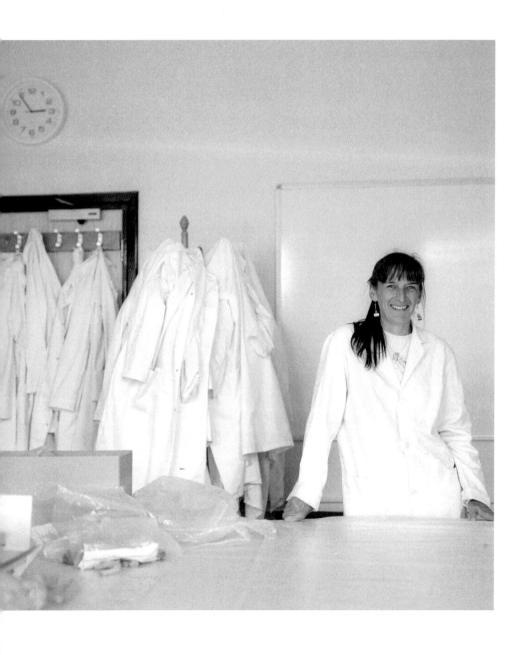

CHARLOTTE ROBERTS made no headway with science at school but trained as a nurse – her mother's profession – after arts A-levels. She returned to study after a number of years in the health service. A stint on an archaeological excavation while working in a specialist burns unit in Chepstow awakened her interest in archaeology and she took a degree in the subject at the University of Leicester. There followed a Master's degree at the University of Sheffield and a research assistantship in Bradford, working with a doctor she had first met while in Leicester.

Her first area of research was leprosy and tuberculosis in ancient Britain and her PhD considered the evidence for trauma and its treatment in antiquity. She went on to study a whole range of diseases, using human bones from archaeological sites around the world. Her experience of caring for living patients stands her in good stead today when she is trying to diagnose and interpret disease from signs gleaned from remains hundreds or thousands of years old.

Following a lectureship in 1989 at the University of Bradford and promotion to Senior Lecturer in 1994, she is now Reader in Archaeology and classed as a 'biological anthropologist' at the University of Durham, where she researches evidence of past patterns of disease and connects them to diet, environment and culture. She also teaches undergraduate and postgraduate students. She has been a potholer and rock-climber and is currently a fell-runner. She ran the Everest Marathon in 1999.

Monday 4 February 2002, Durham
Meet with Keith (colleague) and Sarah (PhD student) about a skeleton from Ripon Cathedral dated to the late medieval period. Has a strange chest. Her breast bone is very curved, her ribs seem to be pushed outwards and upwards

and the spinous processes (the lumps you can feel down your back) of some of her vertebrae are flattened. It looks as if she had something bound around her chest – maybe a corset or brace? Sarah has done the detailed recording of the skeleton and is writing it up for publication. We think it would be a good idea to present it at a conference to get some ideas. In April I am off to Buffalo, New York State, to the Annual Paleopathology Association Meeting where we agree I should give a paper. I will get some sticky wax and try and reconstruct the thoracic cavity to see what shape it was. I email several colleagues here and in the USA who may have encountered skeletons whose owners could have worn corsets.

It's hard to interpret any abnormalities we see in skeletons we excavate. They were once living people but the hundreds or thousands of years they were buried contribute to the decay of the soft tissues and all we are left with are the bones. We then try to 'read' the skeleton by comparing what we see with what we know. We record abnormalities, their shape, size, structure and distribution around the skeleton, and compare our findings with medical data. For example, damage to the spine with loss of the vertebrae may lead us to a diagnosis of tuberculosis because we know that it affects the spine more than any other part of the skeleton. However, destruction of the spine may occur in other diseases, although in those other conditions there is often some bone repair not seen in TB. Our methods of diagnosis are limited by the samples. Visual observation, radiography, histology and, more recently, molecular methods of analysis are used, if there is time and money enough.

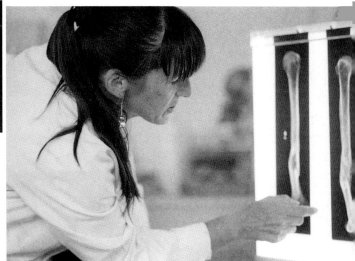

With our lady from Ripon we have a problem because there are few leads to indicate what the abnormality might be. Sometimes we may end up with several scenarios and cannot decide which is the most likely. If only the skeleton could speak.

More often, though, diagnosis is obvious. It is then that we can pool data to explore the origin, evolution and past spread of diseases. For example, from the data currently available from skeletal remains on either side of the Atlantic, we can say that venereal syphilis developed over here *before* Christopher Columbus and his crew sailed to the New World from the Old in 1492, although people used to think that it originated in the Americas and was brought back to the Old World by Columbus in 1493. We can also say that leprosy appears to have its origin in Egypt in the second century AD and tuberculosis in Italy several thousand years ago, but neither infection reached its height until the later medieval period in Europe, with the increase in population density and the stress of urban living conditions.

Wednesday 6 February
I take twelve MSc palaeopathology students to visit a crematorium. Strange for the average person, but educational for students. We go behind the scenes and see the whole process, from the coffin going into the cremator to the

raking out of the bones afterwards and their cremulation, or grinding up. It is informative for people working with human remains from archaeological sites to see all this, a much more controlled process than it would have been in the past. Most fascinating is the size of the bone fragments (large in many cases) that come out of the cremator; they indicate that what we see archaeologically are probably cremated remains that have been badly fragmented during gathering after cremation, burial and excavation. The students find it quite amazing. I first visited this crematorium when I was a student nurse doing a project on 'Disposal of the Dead'. We then visit the recently opened Thackray Medical Museum in Leeds, another coincidence because it is housed in a former geriatric wing of St James's Hospital where I trained to be a nurse in the mid-1970s, when I first left school. The museum is fabulous and traces the development of medicine and surgery, with a focus on the health hazards of living in Leeds in the nineteenth century.

Friday 8 February
Tonight I am doing one of my favourite things – giving a talk, in this case 'Dead People's Bones Do Tell Tales', to the Northumberland Archaeological Group. The place (Newcastle University) is packed. The talk goes well – you can always tell by checking how many people are asleep by the end – and there are lots of those probing questions that I always expect from this type of group.

Tuesday 12 February
A PhD student from the University of Sheffield comes to make casts of teeth from a Jordanian burial I analysed some time ago. Patrick is interested in very early skeletons from this part of the world (and this *is* early – pre-Pottery Neolithic) and particularly in the wear on their teeth, so that he can work out the sort of diet the people were eating and how they made a living. He is looking for skeletons of the right period from the Middle East, one of the earliest sites of domestication of plants and animals around eight thousand years ago.

Saturday 16 February
My favourite sport. We travel (Stewart, my partner, and Kip, our border collie dog) to just south-west of Edinburgh to run a fell race. Overweight for much of my adolescence, I never got chosen for teams and this left me demoralised and unenthusiastic about sports, except horse riding. My sports teachers

would be very surprised to see me now. This race is only six miles but there is a climb of 2,500 feet in total, which makes it a tough little number. Last year with the foot and mouth crisis we hardly got on the fells (especially in County Durham) and our fell fitness is not great. I started fell-walking in the 1970s but never thought I'd be running on hills in the 1990s and beyond. Fell-running must be one of the hardest sports around and we're not relishing the thought of the race but we've got to start somewhere! We are bused to the start and kindly provided with tents to shelter us from the biting wind that is blowing across the open landscape of the Carnethy Hills. The race is hard and though there are supposed to be five hills, there must be at least eight. There are some incredible athletes in this sport. I don't class myself in this group but I do excel in the longer events; stamina seems to be something older women have. Prizes are given and we then call briefly in on some friends in Edinburgh before going to the Fell Race Ceilidh for a couple of hours. The things you have to like with fell-running are beer and dancing.

Monday 18 February
Ellen, one of my PhD students, has just flown in from Hawaii via Atlanta in the United States. She works at the US Army Identification Laboratory. Their work concerns the location, recovery and identification of US victims of conflict in parts of south-east Asia such as Vietnam. For her PhD she is looking at the patterns of fractures in military personnel killed in aircraft crashes over recent years. A number of different aircraft are included in her study, with knowledge of how people were seated, how fast the plane was flying, and other factors important in generating the fractures. Who knows, in the future this work may be used to improve the design and flying of aircraft. We meet to discuss some of the data she has collected in Washington DC where records are very detailed and include radiographs of the fractures.

Wednesday 20 February
Meet with Marie-Catherine, a Canadian PhD student, in order to discuss her progress. She is preparing papers for two conferences in the United States and Sheffield. She is steaming ahead with research on (anonymised) medical records of children admitted to Stannington tuberculosis sanatorium in north-east England during the first half of last century. It is a fascinating set of data. The detailed profiles of each child provide information on their family background, age and sex, where they contracted their TB, when they were

admitted and discharged, and what treatment they had. This sort of data is beyond our grasp when simply examining old skeletons. I have a real interest in TB and have recently completed a book about its history, *Bioarchaeology of Tuberculosis: A global perspective on a re-emerging disease*, with a colleague in America – Jane Buikstra of the University of New Mexico. My first encounter with the disease was when I nursed a person with TB, a man in his 40s, who eventually died. Most people today are familiar with TB: they either have a relative who had it or they know about the increasing problem in both developing and developed countries – and the crisis is far from over. Only if the world's governments were to get rid of poverty and HIV and develop new drugs, would we see a decline in the disease.

Thursday 21 February
My posture is poor. I slouch and get neck stiffness and pain after sitting for long hours. I am recommended the Alexander Technique by my former aromatherapist. Today is my first lesson, one to one. Judith is friendly and immediately works out some of my problems. This technique is to help with posture and to make you realise your bad habits. I sit in front of a computer for a lot of my working day and that, accompanied by the pressure of being an academic, has led to a tensing of my upper body. Let's see if it makes a difference (it does).

Thursday 28 February
I host a university seminar given by my old mentor Keith Manchester from the University of Bradford. It's part of a series in which a medical historian and a palaeopathologist talk about the same disease but use different forms of evidence. Tonight it is leprosy. This is still plaguing some parts of the world, especially South America, India and China, although antibiotic treatment is available. The deformity and disability that can result may, of course, be extensive. It goes with the stigma attached to the word 'leper'. The seminar is well received. Keith is essentially retired from academia but he still has the spark that so many academics lack.

Wednesday 13 and Sunday 17 March
Wednesday is one of the running club's training nights. This week we propose a run along part of the old railway track network of County Durham. Originally used for the coal industry, long since gone, this network now

provides a haven for walkers, runners, horse riders and mountain bikers. Fifteen of us are rewarded with a clear starry night – even the odd owl hooting! It is such a joy to do this rather than face the roads of Durham although we have to wear head torches to see our way.

On Sunday we host a run from our house. It's St Patrick's Day and everybody has to wear something green. We run mostly off-road. This is in sharp contrast to last year when we had the same run just as the foot and mouth crisis was starting and had to be careful where we went. Lots of Guinness is consumed.

Friday 22 March
Term finished last week. A sense of freedom to get on with research – five weeks of Easter vacation which, of course, also means catching up on administration that could not be done in term-time, besides trying to have a rest. I must apply for a few years of research monies, though fortunately I have just heard that I have research leave from October 2002 to January 2003 – no more teaching until next January.

Saturday to Monday 23–25 March, Sheffield
Conference on tuberculosis. I need to attend because of our book. There might be something new that could be included in the final draft. Marie-Catherine is also speaking. It is not the usual group of people who are my peers at conferences, as none of them uses skeletal evidence to consider the prehistory and history of tuberculosis. This lot are mostly people working with documentary evidence from the late nineteenth and twentieth centuries. I meet people working on the history of TB in different countries of the world and even a PhD student from the Department of Sociology at Durham who is looking at homoeopathic treatments for TB in the past.

Monday to Saturday 8–13 April, Buffalo, New York State
The most important meeting of the year – the annual meeting of the American Association of Physical Anthropologists and the Paleopathology Association. It's time to catch up with colleagues, see the latest developments in the field and recharge my enthusiasm for the subject. I share a room with Anne Grauer, whom I met in England in the early 1980s when she was doing her PhD. We have remained good friends and colleagues. Our latest project is a book on medieval women's health, as gleaned from skeletal and documentary evidence. I present the paper on the skeleton from Ripon Cathedral with no further

suggestions as to the cause of this lady's chest deformity. I believe that it is a pathological condition called *Pectus carinatum* which has seen some attempt at treatment. Must write this up for publication when I get back.

By chance, the reviews of the TB book from the publisher's readers come through at the conference. We are able to attend to the comments. I also go to a meeting on the History of Health in Europe project. Co-ordinated by three American colleagues and partially funded by the National Science Foundation, the project aims to consider the health of past European populations. This means collaborating with people from many different countries with different cultures and languages and collating good data on evidence for disease in skeletons through time. Integrating ecological information such as environment, climate and diet to understand the patterns of disease will help us interpret what we find. It is an ambitious and complex effort which will take several years. We don't have a grip on health through time in Europe yet – only the snapshots provided by individual studies on specific populations, time periods and places. But this project has vision.

Sunday to Tuesday 14–16 April, Albany
Meeting over. I fly on to visit the State University of New York at Plattsburgh and give a lecture. Mark Cohen, who has invited me, has done inspiring work on health at the transition from hunting and gathering to agriculture, and during the development of urbanism and industrialisation.

We visit Saranac Lake in the Adirondack Mountains about an hour from Plattsburgh. This was where the first TB sanatorium opened in the United States in the late nineteenth century. Edward Livingstone Trudeau, a doctor, built 'cure cottages' where victims came and attempted to recover with rest, fresh air and a good diet. At 1,600 feet above sea level, the air was beneficial and thousands came for the 'cure'. Saranac Lake has developed over the years but the original cure cottages are still there. They can be identified by their characteristic verandahs where people rested outside for long periods. The next day I visit the 'bone lab' and see some of the Mayan skeletons that Mark curates there and then I give a talk on 'Tuberculosis: Past and Present' for some 50 people at the college.

Thursday 2 May, Nottingham
Travel with a colleague Paul Budd to the British Geological Survey to meet Simon Mays for a discussion on future research. We meet here because it is

logistically easier (about half-way between Durham and Portsmouth) but also because some of the analysis will be undertaken here. Simon and I are particularly interested in venereal syphilis in skeletons in Britain before Christopher Columbus. Most are located in cemeteries in eastern England and on major rivers or in ports. Recent research by Paul using oxygen isotope analysis has shown that a woman with the infection buried in Essex had grown up in Norway. The analysis indicates that the ratios of different isotopes of oxygen in her teeth are consistent with the ratios in water in Norway. We wonder whether an origin across the Channel and North Sea could be claimed for all these syphilitic individuals. The starting point is structuring the project and deciding who to ask for money. Unfortunately the Natural Environmental Research Council has just cancelled its July grant round due to lack of funds so we think about the Wellcome Trust as a possibility. The research may contribute to the much larger debate about where and when venereal syphilis originated and where it then went to – and whether Columbus had anything to do with it at all!

Friday 24 May
After a distressing day in Leicester, not being able to breathe for most of it, I resort to the low-dose steroid inhaler for my asthma which the doctor gave me three weeks ago. A week later I am at the homoeopath and admitting having to do this but feeling much better. She is still convinced that she will cure me of my asthma and I have every faith in her. She prescribes some 'calming' remedies in preparation for examiners' meetings I will be chairing next week (they definitely help).

Wednesday and Thursday 19–20 June
I am now external examiner at Leicester, my old university. It seems strange to think that in 1982 I graduated and in 2002 I am their examiner. This system in UK universities (unheard of in the States) exists to ensure that standards between universities and between subjects are similar. It is a very time-consuming business but is perhaps fairer for students. After two internal examiners have marked each piece of work that counts towards the final degree, the external examiners moderate the marking and check consistency. Securing external examiners for each course, and all subjects and universities, can be difficult.

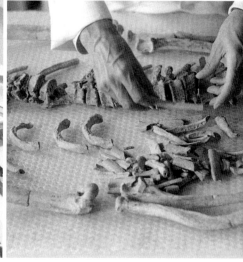

Monday 8 July, Bilbao, Spain

The final draft of the book on tuberculosis goes to the publishers; the index for a leprosy book, *The Past and Present of Leprosy: Archaeological, historical, palaeopathological and clinical approaches* (the proceedings of a conference I hosted in 1999) is done and I fly to Spain. A colleague has part-ownership of a twelfth-century palace in a small village near Zaragoza. He is conducting fieldwork with Durham students and I am joining in for two weeks. Stewart has come too. The palace is stunning and is slowly being renovated. The area is arid but there are olive and almond trees and vineyards. A typical day is: start work at 9 am, break at 11 am, lunch at 1 pm followed by a siesta until 5 pm and then start work again until 8 pm. We walk across fields, wash the finds and mark them. Chris has established a map of the fields and gained permission from many farmers. We walk in ordered lines for a certain amount of time, determined by the size of the field, and pick up any prehistoric to modern finds. It is a successful first season. Prehistoric, Roman and medieval sites are suspected on the basis of the density and type of finds. In subsequent years excavation may take place. Evenings from about 9 to 11 pm are spent eating great food and drinking very cheap but palatable wine. It's a rather pleasant existence. Although I start work on the third edition of *The Archaeology of Disease*

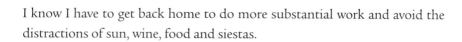

I know I have to get back home to do more substantial work and avoid the distractions of sun, wine, food and siestas.

Thursday to Wednesday 1–7 August, Durham

Anne arrives from Chicago for a week to discuss the book on medieval English women's health that we have been pontificating about for several years now. It is a productive time where we thrash out the chapters and subheadings. Anne also agrees to dog-sit for us while we go and do a fell race in Borrowdale in the Lake District. This is one of my favourites and I was determined to complete it again, having not been running much this year because of asthma. It's seventeen miles, 6,500 feet of ascent, and takes in Scafell Pike, Great Gable and Dale Head in a circular route (and the record is just over 2.5 hours). The day is hot, very hot, and many people retire but I manage to complete the race.

Tuesday to Sunday 27 August–1 September, Coimbra, Portugal

We fly off to Portugal for the Paleopathology Association European Meeting (to be held in Durham in 2004). Coimbra has the oldest university in Portugal and is a wonderful city set on very steep hills. We stay at the Astoria Hotel which has a park just down the road for running. The conference attracts over 200 participants and is very successful – delegates talk about most diseases that affect the skeleton. My paper is on the history of leprosy in Britain and focuses on a possible link between the decline of leprosy in the fourteenth century and the rise of tuberculosis. Recent research on twentieth-century leprosy and tuberculosis rates in Texas, USA, has indicated there isn't such a link. In Britain we do not as yet have the absolute frequency data from skeletons of this period to explore the subject further but it certainly needs to be done. I stress this point but also discuss the need to use biomolecular methods of diagnosis to consider the strain of the tuberculous organism that people were suffering from way back in the Roman period, the earliest evidence of tuberculosis we have in Britain – for example, is it different from the modern strain? Another piece of interesting research, reported at the conference by a German team, used ancient DNA analysis to identify in Egyptian mummies the specific organism causing tuberculosis. This type of research has enhanced our understanding of past disease considerably.

Monday 2 September, London
Back to Brunel University to attend the last day of the international conference on Holocene Catastrophes and Recovery. By 'catastrophes' we mean major events that have changed the world, such as a volcanic eruption, a massive flood, a change in climate, the transition to agriculture from hunter–gathering, or the rise of urbanism. I speak on health in Britain at the time of the extension of urbanisation in the late medieval period. This sort of multidisciplinary conference, with delegates from geography, geology, anthropology and archaeology, encourages researchers to cross the boundaries of their discipline and delve into subject areas that may be helpful to understanding their own. For example, a discussion by climatologists on a rise or decline in global temperature has implications for health and may explain sudden appearances of disease.

Monday 30 September, Durham
For the next few months I am blessed with a sabbatical and aim to complete the third edition of *The Archaeology of Disease,* begin a new book, write some papers and apply for some grants. The proofs of another book, *Health and Disease in Britain: Prehistory to the present day,* which I senior-authored with a colleague, Margaret Cox, should arrive for checking. I will be glad to see this on the bookshelves as it has been a mountain of a book to compile. Using primarily skeletal evidence for disease, it charts the health of the

British and tries to explain what we see in terms of cultural factors present at the time, such as settlement patterns, housing, diet and economy. It's a book that is long overdue and we hope that it will be useful for future researchers. My application to join the Institute of Teaching and Learning has been accepted. After teaching full-time for nearly thirteen years I must be doing something right.

biophysicist
Tanniemola Liverpool

TANNIEMOLA LIVERPOOL was born in London, but moved to Sierra Leone as a small child and then lived in Nigeria, returning to the UK as a teenager in the 1980s. His father was a university mathematician and he, in turn, excelled in maths and then concentrated on physics at university. Following a PhD in theoretical physics at Cambridge, he did post-doctoral work in Germany and held a Marie Curie Research Fellowship in Paris from 1998–2000. He then took up a Royal Society University Research Fellowship at Imperial College London, working on condensed matter theory. In particular, he tries to understand the behaviour of solutions containing long chain molecules and how their various entanglements affect the flow properties of the liquid. This takes him into areas as diverse as chemical engineering, cell biology and biophysics, albeit using the tools of a theoretical physicist. Understanding how DNA strands can be copied, for example, is much more than a matter of chemistry. It involves many puzzles about how multiply coiled lengths of the DNA helix can be unwound, separated, copied and repackaged, without simply ending up with something which looks like the wires coming out of the back of a computer.

His diary describes an extended visit to California, with new opportunities for scientific interaction and for reflecting on whether returning to life in London is bearable.

Monday 4 February 2002, Santa Barbara, California
I've flown into Los Angeles and caught the Santa Barbara Airbus to Goleta, arriving at about 10 pm absolutely exhausted.

I'm staying at Berkshire Terrace apartments, luxury compared with my tiny room in a shared flat in London. I have a large one-bedroom apartment with a walk-in wardrobe that is almost as large as my bedroom back home.

There is an unheated swimming pool in the complex which is nice to look at but appears rather cold. I don't think I'll be doing much swimming there.

I am spending the next five months in the Institute for Theoretical Physics (ITP) at the University of California, Santa Barbara, taking part in a workshop on the dynamics of complex and macromolecular fluids. I am looking forward to the workshop. Almost all the scientific 'heavyweights' working on the dynamics of complex fluids will be in town at some point while I'm here. I am going to meet lots of people whose names I know only from their papers, as well as catch up with old friends.

So what are complex fluids? They are condensed states of matter (that is, not gases) that have properties of both liquids and solids. This is generally due to some structure at an intermediate 'mesoscopic' scale, between the 'microscopic' or atomic scale and our 'macroscopic' human scale: for example – and this will be the focus of much of the meeting – the solutions of the long chain molecules called polymers. Plastics and rubber are polymers and so are the crucial biological substances, DNA and proteins. Understanding the properties of polymers under flow has many applications. An obvious one is in the chemical processing industry: a five per cent improvement in efficiency through a better understanding of flow properties can save millions of pounds.

Even though the building blocks which make up these materials can be very different, there are a number of universal features which can be used to understand how they behave when they are pushed and pulled around. We can predict with some success, for example, which are liquid and which are rubbery or brittle. My challenge, and that of other physicists in my field, is to identify which properties of these materials don't depend on the details of their basic building blocks, their chemical structure.

Quite a bit of progress has already been made, leading to a number of Nobel Prizes. If one thinks of polymers in solution as an entangled mesh of microscopic strings, it turns out, quite amazingly (with some reflection, of course), that it is possible to understand fairly well how a human-sized amount

of a material made up of polymers would behave if you squeezed it or stretched it. A key idea in our current level of understanding was put forward by Pierre-Gilles de Gennes of the Collège de France in Paris, expanding on earlier work by Sam Edwards in Cambridge. De Gennes, who won the Nobel Prize for Physics in 1991 for this and many other original ideas, suggested that because of the mesh of surrounding polymers, an entangled polymer could move only by slithering along its contour like a snake. He called this reptilian movement 'reptation'. A new kind of activated reptation is an important process in the materials I study.

Tuesday 5 February
My office is great. I've got a fantastic view of the Pacific Ocean. The ITP is near the edge of a small cliff overlooking the sea. The beach reminds me a little bit of Lumley beach in Freetown where I spent some of my childhood. As I am spending more than three months at the ITP, I get an office to myself on the ground floor close to the exit.

Every visitor has to go through an orientation. There is a very nice group of administrative staff at the ITP who lead me through mine. I was here three and a half years ago for a workshop on charged polymers so it is a sort of refresher for me. I remember Deborah Storm and Monica Curry from my last visit. As far as I am concerned, the most important part is receiving my coffee mug and instructions on how to get coffee, essential fuel for my brain.

I meet the organisers, Tom McLeish and David Morse from the University of Leeds and the University of Minnesota respectively, whom I've met before, and Fred MacKintosh from the Vrije Universitaet in Amsterdam, whom I know only from his papers. The workshop will have a mixture of theoretical physicists, like me, as well as experimental physicists and chemical engineers. They explain that they intend to have four focused sessions of the workshop with lots of seminars and discussions, separated by 'lighter' periods where more 'work' and less discussion might be the order of the day. The first of these intense sessions is on semiflexible polymers and biopolymers, which fits very nicely with my recent research on the dynamics of semiflexible biopolymers.

Semiflexible? Many of the gross physical properties of polymers have been well understood by thinking of them as totally floppy microscopic strings. But more recent experiments on some biopolymers, called 'thin' filaments, have shown that the degree of floppiness or rigidity of the strings has important consequences for their macroscopic properties. Polymers which have a finite floppiness are called semiflexible. These thin bio-filaments are a major part of the cytoskeleton of cells in many organisms. This is a collection of proteins which supports the cell internally and moves other molecules around inside cells. So the contents of cells are also complex fluids. Recent experiments in the research group of a friend, Josef Käs, at the University of Texas in Austin, suggest that a clearer understanding of this complex fluid could lead to better and earlier diagnosis of some cancers.

Another very important difference between the complex fluid inside the cell and a normal polymer solution is that the cell is 'active'. Proteins called molecular motors, interacting with a number of protein filaments, turn chemical energy into work. These types of protein are essential for the movement of all living organisms, from bacteria to whales.

I think that these 'active' complex fluids are very exciting. I have already published some work on them and intend to do some more while I am in Santa Barbara. Not only are there many possible practical applications but it seems that they are dramatically different from normal 'passive' complex fluids. New ways of thinking have to be developed to understand them.

Thursday 7 February
An old friend, Chris Wiggins, arrives. His office is just next to mine. I met Chris several years ago when we were both young, green physicists, neither of us organised enough to submit our abstracts for the American Physical Society meeting and therefore relegated to poster sessions. We also overlapped as post-docs in Paris. He works on the dynamics of semiflexible filaments too.

Chris and a number of other people are sceptical about a new aspect of the 'longitudinal' dynamics of fluctuating semiflexible filaments discovered recently. It takes a lot of energy to stretch the filaments. This means that movements which bend them become coupled to those which stretch them, and there is a timescale associated with this coupling which has been ignored in the literature until recently. However, a new paper takes this into account and leads to a modification of the overall dynamics, although the interpretation offered is still controversial. I am a believer but there are several unbelievers, like Chris, who are taking part in the complex fluids program. This is the kind of thing we hope to sort out over the next few weeks.

Friday 15 February
Since it's a Friday, a group of us from the ITP decide to go for a drink in the evening in Isla Vista, called IV by everyone, which is a small community adjoining the university campus. It is dominated by undergraduate student housing. As it is illegal to sell alcohol to people under 21 in the USA, a significant fraction of the undergraduate population cannot drink alcohol legally and we can only find two establishments that serve beer on Pardell Road, the main street in IV. After a meal, we decide to take a walk down to the beach and head to De la Playa road which runs along the cliff. There is a bunch of 'rich' student houses along the road facing the sea which seem to have parties going on. I see why UCSB has a reputation for being a party university. Walking along De la Playa, I keep getting asked for marijuana. I wonder why? After the third request, we decide to call it a day and go home.

Saturday 16 February
Having a quiet weekend of reflection. I'm missing home. I certainly don't miss my tiny room and the crap quality of life in London.

Tuesday 19 February
I receive the referees' report from a paper I have submitted to *Physical Review Letters*, the most prestigious journal in physics. The referees agree that while the paper should be published, it doesn't merit the broad scope of PRL and I've been offered a regular article by *Physical Review E*, which will be read by fewer people. I am a bit miffed as I think I have a very good theoretical explanation for a recent experiment that has just got published in the more desirable journal. If the experiment is good enough, why isn't the theory? In any case, I think it merits at least a Rapid Communication (fast-track publication). But

I cannot be bothered to fight with an editor about this so I'll just accept the verdict. Some of the referees' comments are useful though.

Thursday 21 February
I give a talk today on the dynamics of mixtures of bio-filaments and molecular motors. It isn't the best I've ever given. I often leave my preparation to the last minute, which leads to the very variable quality of my talks. They can be very good, so I've been told. Or they can be very bad. This one is somewhere in between. It happens because I put more effort into doing research than in presenting it to others. It is a bad habit, as presenting one's work is an important part of science.

Because of the audience I could go into more of the gory technical details than I usually do in talks. Over the last couple of years I have developed some relatively simple physical arguments which I use to talk about the results without going into details. Now I have an audience who would appreciate the details but I haven't really thought about presenting a more technical talk.

Friday 22 February
We have had some lovely days recently. Even though it's been sunny since I arrived, it hasn't necessarily been that warm. This week it's been about 80 degrees most of the time. I've got a bike and am cycling into work. It's a nice ride from my flat. This is the (scientific) life!

Tuesday 26 February
Over dinner with Chris and Rony Granek, another 'longitudinal' sceptic, we continue our usual intellectual tussle over the longitudinal dynamics question. This seems to have been a constant topic of conversation during the last two weeks. I think we have come to some sort of compromise. They agree that there must be qualitative differences between the 'true' longitudinal dynamics and earlier approximations, but reserve their judgement on whether the correction I and others believe in gives the exact answers.

Thursday 28 February
I have started discussing with Cristina Marchetti from the University of Syracuse about deriving coarse-grained models of the dynamics of filaments and motors from more microscopic models. We want to look at the types of steady state that can be formed by mixtures of filaments and motors. We have

been inspired by a very nice paper from Paris about bundles of polar filaments and motors. Cristina is an expert on the dynamics of flux lines in superconductors. She is at the ITP because there is an interesting overlap between superconductors and complex fluids. Superconductors are substances that below a certain temperature conduct electricity without resistance; they are perfect conductors. At a high enough temperature, when a certain type of superconductor is put in a magnetic field, the field penetrates the superconductor at particular places in bundles of magnetic flux called vortex or flux lines. This is called the 'mixed' state, because even though under these conditions portions of the material are superconducting, there are other regions (that the magnetic field in the form of flux lines has penetrated) which are in the 'normal' state. A normal state refers to the one that is manifest at very high temperatures when not every single part of the material is a perfect conductor. Unsurprisingly, the mixed state is – in a rough sense – a mixture of normal and superconducting states. Under an applied electric current, the vortices move and dissipate energy and the material develops a finite resistance. It turns out that, like polymers, these flux lines get entangled and this entanglement affects their dynamics.

Saturday 2 March
Cristina is returning to Syracuse but we agree to continue the collaboration via email.

Tuesday 5 March
I receive some calculations to check from Paolo Pierobon, a research student who has been working with me since October last year. He is Italian and in the final year of his Laurea, which is the Italian first degree, involving a year of original research. He is on the ERASMUS exchange programme which allows European students to spend a year away from their home institution which for him is the University of Padua. We are communicating by email at the moment but he will also come and spend a month at the ITP in April and May.

I have suggested that Paolo work on collective phenomena in active membranes. Membranes play a key role in partitioning cells. We would like to understand better the active cellular processes, such as shape changes of certain organelles inside the cells of higher organisms, or even the global shape changes that occur in cell division. These are rather complicated systems so we will be starting with the simpler problem of looking at interactions between proteins which can move around while embedded in a membrane. Since we are interested in active processes, we will be looking at the dynamics of proteins on the membrane. It seems to be progressing quite well.

Wednesday 7 March

Feeling depressed. I've been working on a problem in collaboration with Tom McLeish at Leeds and Meredith Betterton at New York University. It looked as if the research was going to produce something interesting and unexpected but instead the result is rather predictable. This is the problem: when cells divide, they have to make two copies of DNA for the two daughter cells. Since DNA is a polymer, these copies will be entangled and difficult to separate. This will slow down cell division considerably. Nature has dealt with this problem by developing another molecular motor called Topoisomerase II which breaks the DNA strands and passes them through one another and then reconnects them. We had developed a model describing how this active disentangling affects the dynamics of the DNA which seemed to indicate that it was qualitatively different. It was looking very exciting. Maybe we could get an article in *Nature*! Sadly, a more careful analysis shows that it is essentially the same as without the motor, only faster, which is good for cell division but less interesting for a physicist.

Monday 11 March

I guess I'm a city person. I miss the vibrancy and cultural diversity of London. I'm even thinking fondly of the Tube! I certainly don't miss the rain. The weather here is nice, the quality of life for me as an academic is much better but the people seem too one-dimensional. Frankly, I'm finding Santa B a bit boring. Maybe I'd like it better in a bigger city.

Tuesday 12 March, Huntsville, Alabama

I arrive in Huntsville where the National Society of Black Physicists (NSBP) and National Conference of Black Physics Students will be having its annual meeting. The NSBP is a society of African-American physicists and exists to act as a support structure and to promote the interests of physicists of colour in the USA. Keith Jackson and Lawrence Norris, who are on the executive committee of the NSBP, have asked me to give a talk for a general physics audience about my research. I am also very interested in seeing how the NSBP works and what sort of outreach projects it is undertaking.

Wednesday 13 March

Something interesting at the conference today. In one of the sessions, I overhear a man talking about Sierra Leone and I go over to talk to him. I introduce myself as also of Sierra Leonean origin and he tells me his name: Ahovi Kponou from the Brookhaven National Laboratory. What a surprise! I have known him since I was a kid but it's been about 20 years since I last saw him.

Both he, in the physics department, and my dad, in the mathematics department, were lecturers in the 70s at the Fourah Bay College of the University of Sierra Leone. His son Ahovi Junior was my classmate in primary school. I remember that we were great rivals. Both our families left Sierra Leone at the end of the 70s. Apparently Ahovi Jr is working on Wall Street in New York. Ahovi Sr gives me his details. I will have to give him a call.

Thursday 14 March

The meeting is interesting and provides much food for thought. I didn't know how few African-American professors were to be found in top US universities. Apparently there are only twelve (0.6 per cent) in the top 50 US universities ranked according to funding.

Friday 15 March, Santa Barbara

My sister, Saweda, arrives to spend the spring break with me. An economist, she started graduate work in development studies at the University of Iowa in August last year. She's been stuck in the midwest and has never been to the west coast of the USA. I am going to try to be a good host and show her around a bit.

Monday 18 March, Indianapolis

I have to leave Saweda alone in Santa Barbara and go to the American Physical Society meeting which is taking place here in Indianapolis from 18–23 March. It is the largest physics meeting in the USA, with over 5,000 participants. I don't like such big meetings – it seems impossible to find the time and space to talk about research and it ends up being more or less a social event. Nevertheless, as I am in the USA, I am down to give two ten-minute presentations.

Tuesday 19 March

My first talk on motor/filament mixtures is a disaster. My usual problem – lack of preparation. In ten minutes, you really have to be absolutely organised and I am not. I get only one question, which is what I deserve for such an awful talk. Later on in the evening, I go out with old friends and drown my sorrows in a few beers.

Wednesday 20 March

My second talk on the properties of a model for DNA goes rather better. Quite a lot of questions. I catch the plane back to Santa Barbara.

Monday 1 April, Santa Barbara

I've been evicted from my office. Someone called Stephen Hawking is visiting the ITP this week. My office is on the ground floor near the side exit. When he visits it is generally allocated to him. For this week I'm happy to squat elsewhere.

Wednesday 3 April

Today is a big day for the ITP. At 2 pm Hawking gives an extremely well-attended seminar on 'Why does inflation start at the top of the hill?' I can't say I understand the title.

The ITP has regular evening public lectures for a general audience by scientists who are good communicators. This evening there is a wonderfully erudite lecture by Frank Wilczek, a professor from MIT, on 'the world's numerical recipe'. He emphasises the importance of symmetry or 'harmony' in the formulation of the fundamental laws of modern physics. He begins with

early attempts by the ancients to explain the world using patterns in numbers and ends with the modern 'gauge' theory of Quantum Chromodynamics (QCD) which can be understood in terms of symmetries of more complicated mathematical objects.

Frank Wilczek is the former graduate student of the director of the ITP, David Gross, and they are considered almost sure bets for a Nobel Prize in the near future. By discovering asymptotic freedom, they showed that QCD was a good theory for the 'strong' interactions which hold atomic nuclei together. Asymptotic freedom explains why quarks and gluons inside protons and neutrons, like members of the same family, behave like free particles when they are close together but feel much stronger forces when they are separated.

David Gross now works on string theory and since his office is between the coffee-maker and my office, I often see him sitting and thinking in his office to a background of classical music.

Friday 5 April
I move back into my office. Someone points out that I can now say that I took over Stephen Hawking's chair. Gilda, my girlfriend, arrives today. She's just spent a few days in New York and will manage ten days with me in Santa Barbara.

Wednesday 10 April
Feeling very positive. The work with Cristina on the polar filaments and motors is going rather well. We have a novel way of looking at the dynamics

of the filaments. A nice 'side-effect' is that the formalism can also be used to treat the dynamics of simple liquid crystals. Liquid crystals are also complex fluids which, even though they flow like liquids, have axes of symmetry and crystalline order like solids.

Wednesday 17 April

I think I saw some whales from the cliff during my jog today.

I've been shortlisted for a lectureship at the University of Leeds and the interview is on 15 May. This means that I'll have to return to the UK when Paolo is here. A shame. There will be presentations by the candidates on 14 May and an interview on the 15th.

Gilda leaves and Paolo arrives.

Tuesday 14 May, Leeds

Interview. My talk is the second one in a series of seven from the candidates. This time I've done the proper preparation and the talk goes well.

Friday 17 May

I get a phone call from the head of department at Leeds offering me the job, on the condition that I bring my Royal Society Fellowship with me. Now it's time for some soul-searching and I've only got one week to make up my mind. Leeds is one of the centres for complex fluids in the UK, so scientifically it will be a good move. But I'll have to leave London. That's tough! For family reasons, cultural reasons, it will be very hard to leave. I know a little of what to expect because I've lived in the North before, having gone to school in Liverpool.

As far as I am concerned, for a black person, London is by far the best place to live in Europe. I speak from experience. I've visited most of Europe's major cities and spent three great years in Germany and two fun years in Paris. For whatever reason, London, uniquely in Europe, seems to have that cultural space which allows me to express myself completely. Nonetheless the fact that London life is pretty impossible on an academic salary makes the choice easier.

It's a hard lesson to learn as an academic scientist. What is good for my science may not be good for other parts of my life. This time it's the science that determines my choice. I hope this won't always be the case.

Saturday 18 May, Santa Barbara
I'm back in California. Hopefully Paolo and I can get some work done now before he heads for London.

Wednesday 22 May
I've taken the job in Leeds.

Friday 31 May
Krishnan, Sharad and Prabhat, friends from London, have arrived for the weekend. They've rented a flat in Los Angeles for two weeks to escape the Jubilee celebrations and have come up to see the central coast. I take them downtown to catch the Santa Barbara vibe. I've only got one address, a bar called Elsie's where by some twist of fate I dominate the pool table, a souvenir of those wasted evenings playing snooker in the sixth form – though I don't remember being particularly good then.

Tuesday 4 June
Cristina and I start writing a first draft of our joint paper on the filament/motor mixtures.

Thursday 27 June, London
I am back. Catch up on the news with my flatmates, Edward and Gordon. Seeing my tiny room, I think maybe it isn't a bad thing that I'm moving to Leeds. London is no place for a scientist.

geneticist

David Gems

DAVID GEMS is a Royal Society University Research Fellow in the Department of Biology at University College London, where he has worked since 1997. Before that he studied genetics at Sussex, but did not at first pursue research. Instead, in the mid-1980s he went to join the revolution in Nicaragua, working as a volunteer in the public works department in Jinotega Province. He also worked in Mexico and Costa Rica and on construction sites in California's Mojave Desert.

Returning to the UK, he took a look at film-making, decided not to pursue it and then returned to science with a PhD at Glasgow and research posts at Imperial College London and the University of Missouri. His main interest is in unravelling the genetics of ageing in nematode worms. He is also a collaborator on a large Wellcome Trust-funded project comparing genetic controls on ageing in worms, fruit flies and mice, which may eventually point the way to an understanding of human ageing. When he is not working in the lab, he thinks and writes about the ethics of biological research on ageing and life extension.

I run a small laboratory which works on the biology of ageing. There are currently six of us: a post-doc, Manoj, three graduate students, Diana, Michelle and Dhaval, an undergraduate project student, Melissa, and me. We study the mechanisms that control the rate of ageing in a simple, short-lived animal – a tiny nematode worm called *Caenorhabditis elegans*.

Thousands of geneticists around the world all work on this one organism, the way that its genes control its development, its shape, its nervous system, its behaviour – and more recently, its longevity. The setting is a big, newly refurbished open-plan laboratory in a building on Gower Street, with benches arranged in a series of bays. We spend most of our time either looking down dissecting microscopes measuring lifespans, constructing multiple mutant strains, or describing developmental phenotypes; or working at computers.

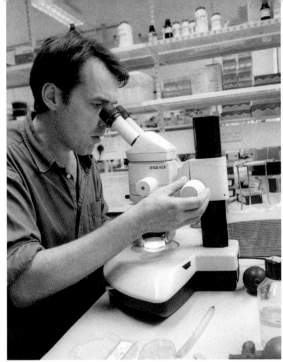

There isn't space here to describe what everybody does, so I will focus on certain things that I am working on with Diana – a couple of threads among many in a complex weave.

Sunday 30 December 2001, East Berlin
Here I am again in Berlin, in Judith's apartment, resting after working through Christmas. It's been pleasant. Last night Judith and I went to a public sauna – something I'd never done. We found one nearby, using the yellow pages. Outside there was a full moon and a bit of thin high cloud and the ground was icy. The sauna was in a grey apartment block on Bornholmerstrasse – the big ring road between Prenzlauerberg and Pankow. I was a bit apprehensive. Judith and I went naked into a big communal shower and then into one of the sauna rooms. Back in the shower a little later, as I gasped at the cold water and chatted with J, a woman came and stood naked right next to me under the cold water, not realising the shock that her bare bottom and thick black bush of pubic hair would cause me – unaccustomed as I was to such a situation. Then others came into the shower, men and women, and for a moment I thought of Bosch's *Garden of Earthly Delights*.

Monday 31 December
Worked in a coffee shop on a review article which is an attempt to integrate the evolutionary theory of ageing with the new genetics of ageing. The deadline is

horribly timed – 7 January. I'll have to work hard on it or have a burst of inspiration during the next few days if it's really going to work. As it is, there is a section on the evolution of ageing and a section on how insulin-like signalling controls ageing – but they don't really speak to each other.

Wednesday 9 January 2002, London
A depressing day. I'd hoped to get the laser microbeam system set up so that Diana could proceed with her studies on the role of the male gonad in regulating lifespan. She needs the laser to perform microsurgery on the worm's gonad, working on larvae that are only a fraction of a millimetre long. Unfortunately, a laser-safe filter cube which I had ordered from the USA turns out to be the wrong size for the microscope. I phoned the US suppliers, who were apologetic and agreed to send out one the right size as quickly as possible.

Diana is in the final stages of a three-year PhD project on the regulation of ageing in *C. elegans* males. All of the previous work on ageing in the worm has focused on the other sex, the hermaphrodite (essentially a female which makes sperm which it uses to fertilise itself). A lab in the USA recently found that the hermaphrodite germline (sperm and eggs and the cells that give rise to them) regulates the rate of their ageing. If these cells are removed by microsurgery with a laser beam, the hermaphrodite lifespan is increased by about half. Diana did some trials on males in a laboratory in Berlin and found that their lifespan was not regulated by the germline. To allow her to investigate further I've acquired the laser. But integrating it with an advanced motorised compound microscope into a laser microbeam system is turning out to be a headache.

Monday 21 January
The replacement laser-safe filter cube arrived in customs and I dealt with the paperwork.

Monday 18 February
Judith is over from Berlin for seven weeks. In the evening we drove over to my parents' house in Paddington to pick up plants for the garden of my flat, which I bought last autumn. Pam (my mother) seemed in a good mood having just finished a new play – a two-hander about Ludwig II of Bavaria and the Empress Elisabeth (Sissi), snowed in at Linderhof. The Sissi part is written for the actress Siân Phillips.

Tuesday 19 February
Every Tuesday afternoon I meet with Diana to discuss her work. Today she had an interesting new finding: male *C. elegans* are resistant to oxidation. We have confirmed the fact that the *C. elegans* males live longer than the hermaphrodites. It is also known that reducing the activity of a hormone system that resembles the human insulin system greatly extends lifespan in both *C. elegans* and fruitflies. We suspect that males may be longer-lived because they have a reduced level of insulin-like activity. And mutant hermaphrodites with reduced insulin-like activity are resistant to stress, such as chemicals which cause oxidation. One theory has it that this sort of stress is actually the cause of ageing. So Diana has been testing whether normal males are resistant to stress.

Tuesday 26 February, Iceland
7.45 am
In a café in Keflavik airport, waiting for my flight home after a stopover here. It's about half an hour before sunrise and there's an orange strip in the eastern sky, over the snow. I'm on my way back from a meeting at the University of Minnesota on the impact of the Human Genome Project on cultural identity. As new biological maps of human groups' histories are drawn up, how will this match their personal stories of where they came from, and when?

I spent yesterday with an old friend, Hildur Helga Sigurdardottir. We went out for a walk with Skotta, her little Icelandic husky. It was very, very cold. We dropped by the school of her son, my godson Odin Páll. He and some other children were playing in the snow, apparently oblivious to the appalling cold. Skotta joined in, taking bites out of the snow. This morning when I left I took with me an enormous cod roe covered in thick veins and wrapped in foil, which Hildur Helga had boiled for me.

Monday 11 March, London
An excellent day: I got the laser microbeam system to work at long last. It burnt a beautiful neat hole in some ink on a microscope slide. Diana was pleased – but then we realised that we still need an eyepiece graticule with targeting crosshairs – which we ordered today – and some specialised filters to control the intensity of the beam.

Monday 18 March
Yesterday I varnished the floor of the front room but in the evening I realised I hated it. J suddenly lost her temper and announced that she would return to Germany. Worn down by this I had a bad night and woke this morning very early, exhausted. We spent some hours in discussion and were reconciled. I wondered if it was her period – she said she thought she was getting it and was stuffing folded toilet paper into her panties. But by the evening it hadn't materialised. She studied my reaction – which wasn't much. A week or so ago she hinted that she might be pregnant, just after I'd got back from work, tired – and I suppose I looked dismayed, because she got upset.

This evening, after a long session of reading, I had a burst of ideas and decided upon a new course of investigation. There is a protein in all animals called Ras, which is a type of switch within the cell, controlling cellular growth. In mammals, if the switch gets stuck in the 'on' position, cancer can result as cells grow and divide wildly. Manoj has been investigating the role of the worm's Ras gene in insulin-like activity. But the same gene also has a well-known role in the development of the nematode vulva – a favourite topic of investigation among *C. elegans*-ologists. I decided to do my own characterisation of the mutant effects of *daf-2* on the mutant effects of Ras, to complement Manoj's studies.

So what is *daf-2*? This is a truly fascinating gene which does many things, including controlling development and ageing. Reduced *daf-2* activity results in more than a doubling of adult lifespan. The *daf-2* gene contains the information for the cell to manufacture a cellular receiver (or receptor) of insulin-like hormones. I will need to learn to identify mutant vulval traits – which means that my main lab work from now until the summer will be microscopy.

The laser: we still haven't sorted out the neutral density filter problem. What we really need is a graded sliding neutral density filter – unfortunately Leica, the microscope manufacturer, doesn't make one. It's rare that anyone wants to attach a laser to a Leica microscope.

Sunday 31 March
This week I was determined to get out of my office and back to the laboratory bench. I worked familiarising myself with our new compound microscope and set up cultures of double mutant worms which have both *daf-2* and an extra-active form of the worm Ras gene. In worms, though, this doesn't cause cancer but instead causes the worm to have extra vulvas (or, more correctly, vulvae). Looking at them I quickly realised that the multivulva trait was less severe in some of the *daf-2* double mutants.

The altered growth switch also leads to one of the cells of the worm's excretory system – the duct cell – being duplicated. I wonder whether mutation of *daf-2* would suppress this duplication. If it does, it would be evidence that the insulin-like system influences the Ras switch. On Friday I looked for the first time at the nematode excretory system, using a specialised form of microscopy called differential interference contrast. With this method one can see within the transparent body of the worm very fine structures whose forms appear with exquisite clarity, like so much moonstone and crystal – yet alive. Even so, the excretory duct cell nucleus proved difficult to see. On Saturday I tried again to find it, and failed. I will try again today.

Judith still thinks she might be pregnant.

Sunday 7 April
A frustrating week. I thought the laser was working, but on Monday Diana came in saying that her attempts at microsurgery had failed. Much of Monday and Tuesday I spent in the darkness of the microscope room trying to get the system to work again. After many attempts to realign the laser, I couldn't fix the fault. Also, I had several more sessions looking for the excretory duct nucleus and although I did manage to find it in a few cases, in most worms I could not.

The most likely reason, I think, is that the set-up of the optics of the microscope was not good enough. I am limited by my poor understanding of the functioning of our complex Leica microscope. I've spent the week working through the thick manual and will stick at it until these problems are solved.

On Wednesday as I scored multivulva worms I realised I was happy that Judith might be pregnant. I phoned her and told her and she was pleased. This morning as we chatted on the phone she remembered that she had a pee-on-a-stick pregnancy tester in her bathroom and went away and did it. It was positive. She sounded happy and relaxed about it.

Today I took Lala (my sister, who has Down's syndrome) to the cinema to see *The Royal Tenenbaums*. I thought it pretty thin and Lala didn't like it much either. Afterwards we went to a Tex-Mex place where she had a margarita and some fajitas.

Wednesday 10 April

Judith went to her gynaecologist today. The embryo, our child, is the size of a baked bean.

Sunday 21 April

I'm taking a break sitting in the sun under the mural on Tottenham Street, after a frustrating five hours failing to see the excretory duct nucleus. Yesterday, using my new knowledge in microscopy, I was able to get beautiful, clear views of the elusive nucleus and had planned to do a trial today, waking up excitedly at 6.30 am. But it all turned to mud. I suspect the agar I was using to mount the worms may have been too old. I'll try again in a bit, using fresh agar.

Evening

I tried yet again looking at the same mutants, using fresh agar pads – and magically the resolution was hugely improved. Within a minute of putting the sample under the microscope, there were the two duct cell nuclei – the cell duplication that I have been looking for over the last month. Wonderful. So the main problem may not have been my poor understanding of the microscope but the preparation of the agar pad.

Monday 22 April

I woke up before 7 am, excited about going to work on cell lineage analysis. Finding the excretory duct cell nucleus has been a breakthrough: it means that my capability as a researcher is considerably extended. As soon as I got to the lab, I took out a double mutant strain to see whether the *daf-2* mutation suppressed the duct cell nucleus duplication. But again I had problems seeing the duct cell nuclei. Demoralised, I returned to looking at single mutants of the Ras switch – before realising that the field diaphragm was poorly adjusted. As soon as I changed this, I had beautiful, pearly, high-resolution images again. I spent much of the day scoring wild-type, single and double-mutant animals. Although in many animals I failed to find the cells, by evening I had scored at least a dozen animals from each genotype successfully. I saw duct cell duplications only when the altered growth switch was not accompanied by mutation in *daf-2*. So the second mutation suppressed the duct cell duplication, confirming that Ras activity *is* influenced by insulin activity.

Friday 26 April
This morning it was raining heavily so I went to work by tube, taking the Northern Line from Chalk Farm to Goodge Street. It was just before 9 am, and the train was crowded. I stood at the opposite side of the door from a young woman with a rather proletarian look to her – fresh-faced, but not especially attractive. At Camden Town an interesting-looking man got on. He was about 60 and his hair, which needed a trim, was white underneath but on top was obviously dyed – a darker grey – and slicked down with hair oil. He wore a jacket of a nondescript tweed. What struck me was that he stood very close to the young woman. She had her back to him and, as I watched, he nonchalantly brushed the back of his hand against her bottom, and looking around with subtle furtiveness, he inched closer to her. I watched him carefully, expecting her to react at any moment and ready to support her. We stopped at Warren Street and she glanced at me without expression. A lot of people got on and shoved the old man up against her and I could no longer see what was happening. At Goodge Street the door that she was crushed against opened and I looked at her again. Her face was completely changed. She looked shocked – her cheeks were flushed and her eyes glittered. I expected her to get off – yet she did not.

Wednesday 15 May
Apparently I have an 85 per cent daughter.

Tuesday 21 May, Paestum, Italy

I'm just south of Naples for the three-day European Worm Meeting. Diana delivered her first major lecture on her work on ageing in male nematodes to an audience of some 300 people and it went well.

Tuesday 4 June, London

Today I had a long discussion with Diana, out of which a new idea emerged. As I have said, removal of the *C. elegans* germline increases hermaphrodite lifespan by about half. Wendy Ng, a clever undergraduate, recently measured lifespan in a number of mutants which lack a germline. Unsurprisingly, these had extended lifespan. But interestingly, some of the mutants she used also happened to contain certain *unc* mutations which normally increase lifespan in males but not in hermaphrodites (*unc* is short for 'uncoordinated': these are mutants with movement problems, often caused by defects in their nervous system). Wendy's findings hinted that these *unc* mutations can also extend lifespan in hermaphrodites which have no germline cells.

This suggests that in the absence of the germline, hermaphrodites behave like males: their lifespans are extended by *unc* mutations. Diana has shown that removing the germline does not increase the lifespan of males – so a life-shortening germline signal is there in hermaphrodites but not in males. So perhaps this germline signal also makes hermaphrodites resistant to the effects of *unc* mutations on lifespan. And as these *unc* mutations affect the nervous system, the germline signal may work by altering the way that the nervous system controls lifespan.

We both got excited about this, and D decided she would look at the effect of removal of the germline by laser surgery on *unc* hermaphrodites, where we might expect the *unc* mutations to increase lifespan. She will also verify Wendy's preliminary results.

Saturday 15 June

Early tomorrow Judith and I leave for Calabria – Italy's toe – for three weeks. It will be the longest break I have had since 1993 – and interesting to see how I endure such a long period of leisure.

Thursday 4 July, Mattinata, Italy

Unalloyed idleness has proved to be too much but spending a few hours each morning working on an essay on the ethics of research into ageing is keeping me in good spirits. We have been on the road and are now in Apulia, staying in a small apartment in a grove of old olive trees. The grounds are nicely gardened. There are white-painted walls planted with geraniums, lots of oleanders, agaves, pines and well-watered lawns – and deafening crickets. The hotter it gets, the louder they chirp. Judith lies inside, sleeping in the heat of the day – on her side with one leg right up as if she is mounting a great rock – with her pregnancy-enlarged bum in her white knickers – and *Die Kleine* floating ominously inside her.

Sunday 14 July, London
Returning to the lab I feel at first a little like a weary old carthorse being harnessed again to his heavy cart. This weekend I've planned a big push to get Diana's papers moving. Yesterday she gave me a rough manuscript listing the greater part of her results in an unstructured form. Out of this we will mould two, or perhaps three, research papers. Yet I don't have the energy to really get started with it. The worst thing is the laser. It still isn't working after *all* this time! I must try again to align it and if this isn't successful I shall have to get someone – and pay them if necessary – to come and make it work.

Saturday 20 July
A better week, mainly because working with Diana's data has been fascinating. It is as if she has been identifying pieces of a great puzzle and now at last we are starting to fit them together. What will the solved puzzle tell us?

Tuesday 23 July, Bregenz, Austria
I'm here to give a talk at a conference on ageing. This evening I arrived in a taxi at the meeting venue, Kloster Mehrerau. There was nobody around but I found an envelope with my name on it, containing a key, stuck on the front door of a dormitory building. The room is spartan, with no phone and strange doors made of heavy frosted glass, with no frame. The outer door is covered over with thin white paper for privacy. Above the bed is a small crucifix bearing a Jesus with one of his arms broken off. Outside there is a low full moon, big and yellow. Just now I walked through the Kloster, which is enormous and apparently quite empty. Great cedars loomed, giving off heavy smells. Snatches of *La Bohème* came on the wind. There was nobody.

Wednesday 24 July
A fairly interesting meeting so far – a number of older American gerontologists are here with their wives and various other people, including a woman in a bright red pant-suit with vaguely kinky-looking laced-up bits at the waist, and cat's-eye contact lenses. She buttonholed me away from the eminent biogerontologist Andrzej Bartke, telling me that she runs a school for women in Russia aimed at teaching them 'to increase their sexual energy'.

Thursday 25 July, return trip
Waiting outside Zurich – the train has broken down. A man in fluorescent orange – a Turk, perhaps – walks alongside the track with a plastic bag and a pair of tongs, picking out old, dried clots of used toilet paper.

Sunday 4 August, Berlin
Have been working intensively on a long manuscript involving analysis of interactions between mutations affecting insulin-like signalling and the male-specific life-extension trait. The work is very absorbing. D's results are full of fascinating details but few clear insights. More light is shone on the odd nature of the *daf-2* insulin receptor gene – but not enough for it all to make sense.

   Judith showed me some pictures of the contents of her womb taken with an advanced ultrasound scanner and in disturbing colour showing a sort of red goblin. Putting my hand on her belly I could feel the tiny creature feebly kicking and wriggling – most strongly when J comes to bed – like a sleeping passenger on a train, awoken by a stop.

Sunday 11 August, London
A good week, dominated by the manuscript, as, upon examination, Diana's data reveals more and more about the regulation of ageing. It happened twice that, as things seem about to fall into place, one piece stopped the puzzle coming together. One especially interesting discovery may be difficult for the non-initiate of worm genetics – but here goes.

   If you reduce insulin-like activity by mutation of the *daf-2* gene, lifespan is greatly increased. This is because functional *daf-2* antagonises other genes, which in turn promotes longevity. We have been trying to understand the role of insulin-like activity in male-specific life-extension mutants, which show changes in different genes again. We have looked at the effect of male-specific

life-extenders in hermaphrodites that already show mutations in one or more of the *daf* genes. Most of the gene combinations have normal lifespans but with one particular combination of *daf* mutations, adding the male-specific life-extension gene produces a doubling of lifespan. Our knowledge of what all these genes normally do suggests that we can now make hermaphrodites behave like males in the way that the nervous system controls ageing. Together with Wendy's observation that *unc* mutations enhance life extension in hermaphrodites that lack a germline, this suggests several new global models for the relationship between gender, germline signalling, insulin signalling and various *daf* genes. I drew out diagrams showing all the different inhibitions and activations and how they may interact. I really think I have got somewhere over the last four days but need to think about it a lot more.

Monday 12 August
An amazing day. I woke very early and went to the lab and, with the new model in mind, I went through D's data again to see how far I can explain its various complexities. At these rare moments of discovery I tend to experience a physical reaction: mainly elation, and a slight anxiety – like vertigo – of being wrong, of being about to fall, and my concentration momentarily fails. This morning this happened again and again, as detail after detail of the data made sense in terms of the new scheme. By about 2 pm I had written up a slightly modified account of the model – about three pages of text and some diagrams – and felt worn out. Although many details remain

uncertain, the core of it appears robust: signalling through two of the *daf* genes regulates the way that the nervous system controls ageing. The data supports the idea that the germline contributes to this and that sex differences in signals from the germline are responsible for the sex-specific effects of neuronal *unc* mutations on lifespan.

Friday 23 August
More time spent aligning the laser. I worked on it last weekend and got it to function quite well, ablating cells with sufficient accuracy. I showed D and she agreed. But it is not quite perfect so I went through the alignment process again only to find that the outcome is worse. Each afternoon I have spent two to three hours attempting to align it and never quite getting it good enough.

Saturday 31 August
Yesterday I spent more time aligning the laser. I managed to improve it quite a bit, using some new tricks I had worked out. Today I tested it again and it seems perfect. D carried out some tests too and was satisfied. Next week some new trials will start, looking at *unc* mutant hermaphrodites. It feels a little like a train which has been stuck between stations for six months but is at last moving again.

physical chemist
Caroline Dessent

CAROLINE DESSENT is a Royal Society University Research Fellow in the Department of Chemistry at the University of York. She studied chemistry at Oxford, followed by a PhD in physical chemistry at Yale, and has worked at York since 1997.

Her special interests are in unusual ions (molecules in which one or more of the atoms have gained or lost an electron and hence carry an electric charge) and in electron transfer processes. The latter are important in understanding chemical processes such as radiation damage to DNA or photosynthesis in plants, as well as for their theoretical interest. The ions she studies are produced as a gas, rather than in a liquid solution. This allows her to investigate their fundamental properties without their behaviour being affected by interactions with the molecules of the liquid. Although they are sometimes found in the earth's atmosphere, interstellar space and ultra-hot plasmas, these ions are often unstable and highly reactive in the laboratory.

To study them, her lab needs specialised instruments, both to generate the ions and to analyse their behaviour, and these have to be designed, financed, and built to order. As her diary relates, moving her research forward depends as much on making these work as on understanding the properties of the exotic chemical species they harbour. It also demonstrates the juggling act required of a scientist trying to build a career while contributing to running a home with a young child.

Tuesday 2 April 2002, York
Back at work today after my week's 'holiday' at home replacing our kitchen. At least Jonathan, my partner, has been replacing the kitchen while I took care of James. I haven't done any chemistry all week. James, who's almost nineteen months, has been quite hard work. He was having a full-body tantrum this morning as I left the house.

No applications from prospective graduate students while I've been away. I'm worried that I won't get a student this year, despite having funding for two. It's frustrating as there isn't much I can do about it – either a student wants to be in your group or you don't get anyone, even when you've got the money.

Why would a student want to work with me? Well, why am I doing this kind of research? It is a specialised interest. If you really want to understand how molecules behave, looking at the molecules as a gas (where the individual molecules are separated) allows you to understand their properties in great detail. Life is simpler in the gas because there are none of the solvent effects which make things harder to follow in liquids. Most gas-phase research to date has been on neutral, uncharged systems because they are the easiest to produce. But the vast majority of molecular systems carry excess electrical charges (that is, they are ions) in solids or liquids. So part of my motivation for studying ions is the challenge of developing instrumental methods that allow these systems to be studied in detail in the gas phase.

I am particularly interested in the study of anions, which are molecules that carry excess electrons, since I am fascinated by the way in which electrons behave within a molecule. One of the future fundamental challenges for chemistry will be developing ways of monitoring how electrons within molecules move or evolve during chemical reactions, something which happens very, very fast. Studies of anions can be a first step in this direction since the behaviour of the excess electron can occasionally be isolated, allowing the electron's reactivity to be monitored.

Instruments aside, my main scientific goal for this week is to sort out what I'm going to do with a theoretical project I've been working on for about a year and am trying to bring to a close. This involves extensive calculations using quantum mechanics to calculate fundamental chemical properties of molecules, such as their geometric structures and energy levels. To do the sums I mainly use one powerful computer program, named GAUSSIAN, which was developed by John Pople and won him a Nobel Prize in 1998. Although the quantum behaviour of systems of more than one elementary particle quickly gets too complex to handle with complete accuracy, this package makes quantum theory calculations on molecules almost routine for many chemists.

The software itself is relatively straightforward to run, but there is still a research element in evaluating when the different levels of theory available within the program – which give different approximations to the 'true' result – work well for a given type of system. I want to establish reliable and efficient ways to calculate the chemical properties of the ionic systems I study experimentally. I plan to run a new batch of test calculations over the next few weeks to double-check my recent results, as there's a discrepancy between the results I've obtained using two different levels of theory and I need to work out which is correct. This will involve running more calculations at a higher level of theory still. At least this should be straightforward and use up the supercomputer's time, not mine.

Thursday 4 April

Good news: a formal application for one of my PhD vacancies from William Boxford. He's a student from Bristol who came to visit me in January. He seemed very enthusiastic but I hadn't heard from him since so I'd pretty much given up hope that he'd apply. His application form indicates that he's also applied to Oxford and Birmingham but at least he hasn't crossed me off his list.

Monday 8 April

The proofs of my *Journal of Physical Chemistry* article arrive this afternoon. Getting the article into press has represented a minor triumph in the battle of Young Researcher versus Established Referee. I submitted the paper last July, and received one excellent review of the manuscript requesting only minor corrections and a second review that was pretty scathing. I had to contend with fairly insulting remarks like: 'This result is very surprising and we have been unable to reproduce this calculation.' This is as damning as comments come, implying that the results are bogus. After reading the review, I repeated the calculations, which checked out fine, and sent the raw data to the editor. The referee then withdrew his initial claim, saying that he had meant he couldn't understand the calculations, not that he couldn't reproduce them. This, along with other comments which seemed to disparage the work, was particularly hard to take, given that I was sure I knew who the referee was (the reviews are supposedly anonymous) and he's someone I'd expected to be sympathetic to my work. Anyway, after two revisions of the manuscript we were able to bury our differences without either side conceding much, although the whole thing has cost time. It feels good to see the work go into print. I only hope it hasn't generated too much bad blood between the hostile referee and me.

I've had a nasty feeling that the proofs would arrive before I'd finished the new test calculations, since they're related to the work I'm publishing. Now I have to concentrate on checking the calculations that have gone into the manuscript and everything is hugely urgent as you're only allowed 24 hours to check proofs. I can drag this out to 48 hours, but that'll be the absolute limit. Nothing runs quickly on our supercomputer when you really need it to. Spend all day retrieving old calculations and editing the results into new files, then sending things to and from the computer, and fighting with the queuing system to get jobs to run. End up bleary-eyed from being at the workstation all day and head home at 7.30 pm to see James before he goes to bed. I should have stayed later and got everything to run, but I can't face making up any more job files. I'll probably regret it tomorrow.

Tuesday 9 April
Finally get everything I need for the paper in proof by 3 pm and, thank God, everything works out OK. It's worth the frenzied effort to check that what's going into print is correct. My battles with the hostile referee have dented my confidence.

Wednesday 10 April
Meet up with Ramsay Kindar who's a salesman for a vacuum hardware firm. We are probably going to buy vacuum pumps from him for the new spectrometer I'm building with Klaus (the Chair of Physical Chemistry). These are vital, as unless there is a near-perfect vacuum inside the instrument, the ions will instantly collide with other air particles and the experiments will be useless. Problem is that Klaus and I can't agree which type of pumps to buy. Klaus wants a more expensive option than the one I have been thinking of. It would be good to have the fancier pumps if we had unlimited funds but I don't think they are essential. Klaus has said that I should buy the ones I think are best, but I know which he wants.

Tuesday 16 April
Back from visiting my parents with James while Jonathan's been away on a selection weekend for the Territorial Army. William Boxford has emailed me to say that he'd like to accept my offer of a PhD position. He'll work on a new project which involves coupling a device called an 'electrospray ion source' to a laser spectrometer. Electrospray is one way of getting ions out of solution and into the gas phase for closer study. My first goal is to study molecules with multiple excess negative charges (multiply charged anions) to see how the charges interact. There will be lots of scope for expanding the experiment as electrospray can produce all sorts of exotic ions in the gas phase, hence allowing you to study them in detail using lasers. Laser light excites the molecules in various ways and we can then record how they lose energy after exposure to the laser. I already have some funds to start building the instrument but I've applied to the Engineering and Physical Sciences Research Council (EPSRC) for a grant to complete the spectrometer.

Wednesday 17 April

I must spend most of today concentrating on the design of the spectrometer I'm building with Klaus. This instrument is known as a photodetachment spectrometer. It is supposed to produce molecules with a single, excess negative electric charge (anions), which will be studied by using a laser to 'photodetach' the excess negative charge. Basically, the laser beam knocks electrons off the ions and we watch what happens afterwards. It is a complicated machine with lots of design trade-offs between different parts. We have to generate the ions, focus them in a beam, using finely tuned electric or magnetic fields, then send them into the part of the machine where they will encounter the laser.

Mark, my post-doc, has been working hard designing the ion-focusing and measuring regions of the spectrometer, but I'm not happy with our design for the ion source. The plasma (basically an ultra-hot gas) which we will use to create the negative ions needs a lot of room to expand. Have we allowed enough? I remember how one of the instruments I worked on during my PhD seemed never to perform properly after we reduced the volume of the source chamber. But it is a precision-engineered piece and if we make it bigger the cost goes up and we will need bigger vacuum pumps to get a good enough vacuum.

I manage to get in by 8.30 am and sift through all the previously published designs of similar spectrometers for three hours before Mark arrives (he's not a morning person). We discuss the source and then he works up a detailed design for the rest of the afternoon. It's crucial that we sort the design out soon as I want to place the order for the chamber.

Thursday 18 April

After James had gone to bed last night, I read over some new publications that I'd taken home. They were instrumental design papers on electrospray spectrometers like the one I plan to build with William next year, but they got me thinking about the design of the other photodetachment instrument. The electrospray spectrometer will incorporate a device called an 'ion-trap' which is used to store large quantities of ions prior to studying their properties. I think it could be a really good thing to include an ion-trap in the photo-detachment spectrometer, too. It may increase the number of ions we can produce, and will certainly make the source perform more reliably. Unreliability has been a real weakness in the performance of previous photo-detachment spectrometers. I wait somewhat impatiently for Mark so that I can run my idea past him. He thinks it should work and says he'll do a literature search to see if anyone else has done this.

Thursday 25 April

Seem to be going around in circles with everything. Our lab is shut down today, as it's being enlarged into the adjoining storeroom. We desperately need more lab space for the new spectrometers but it's frustrating to see the PhD students sitting at their desks while the current spectrometers are out of use. The work is scheduled to take two weeks but I'll be astonished if it's ready in two months. A fresh batch of calculations I'm running on the supercomputer is taking forever, as well as crashing all the time. Until they're finished I'm completely on hold with my theoretical work. Our apparatus design has also stalled. Mark and I are having trouble finding times when we can sit down with Klaus to discuss our ideas, now that the academic term has started. I decide we should concentrate on sourcing another crucial but uncontroversial part of the machine in the meantime but Mark seems distracted with some dissertation work he's finishing off and I get the feeling he's not planning on doing anything much on the spectrometer over the next few days.

Fed up with everything, I decide to go into town to buy picture frames for posters I've chosen in my role as chair of a new committee to improve displays and artwork around the department. Achieving a balance between scientific content and visual appeal has proved to be both a diplomatic and an aesthetic challenge. We've compromised by introducing some new scientific displays (relating to our research) and some artwork (such as digitally morphed pictures). I now have to buy frames to mount things in. Jonathan (and of course James) come along to help. All the poster frames I wanted are sold out at Habitat. Next we go to pick up two huge frames that I've had made to frame some A0-sized research posters. We park on the double yellow lines outside the shop, haul the frames outside, and then discover they don't fit into our boot. What a waste of time. The house is totally trashed when we get home with unwashed dishes, unhoovered floors and damp washing everywhere, and James just doesn't seem to stop screaming. He was screaming when I went out this morning too and he did an awful lot of screaming last night. My mother thinks he's teething and she's probably right but he just seems to be on a very short fuse and hugely impatient at the moment. I can't think where he gets it from.

Friday 26 April

The week ends on a better note as I hear that a paper we submitted to *Physical Chemistry Chemical Physics* two months ago has been accepted for publication with only minor revisions. I edit the paper and mail the revised manuscript back to the journal. I was wrong about Mark yesterday; he made good progress on the design of the new chamber last night and finalised the overall dimensions of the chamber, along with the list of vacuum pumps we need to order. Klaus and I manage to find time to get together and discuss what Mark and I have been doing. He really seems to like my idea about using an ion-trap in the photodetachment spectrometer and agrees that we should incorporate it in the design.

Wednesday 8 May

The academic term is proving much busier than I'd expected and I've spent a lot of time this week doing teaching and administration stuff. Aside from this, Mark and I are working hard on the new instrument. This is definitely the hardest part of my job. I'm not a natural engineer. I really have to make myself do this and keep reminding myself how much I'm going to enjoy using the instrument when it's finished. We have quite a breakthrough in finding a paper by a group of physicists that describes using ultra-low temperature cooling of an ion-trap to produce cold anions for spectroscopy. I have proposed something like this in my EPSRC grant application, so seeing the paper has given me confidence that what I've proposed will work. It also means that we've now got a perfect way to make cold ions for the photodetachment spectrometer. We finally agree on our pumps (the expensive ones) and they are now on order. Waiting for the company to get the source chamber built will be the rate-limiting step in getting the spectrometer working.

Friday 24 May

This morning I receive the referees' reports for my EPSRC grant application. There are four reviews, two excellent, one OK and one that's very mixed. It says the science described is 'world-class and ambitious' but it questions some of the technical details of the proposal in a very vague way. The referee writes things like 'it would be good, if it were to work' without saying why it shouldn't work. This will be tough to respond to but at least the proposal looks as though it has a chance.

Monday 8 July

Jonathan left on Saturday for Grantham and two weeks of basic military training with his TA regiment. My mother and her husband have offered to come up and take care of James while I work. I have lots to do before the end of next week. My summer project student Julie is also starting work then and I'll need to be around to help her. I'm planning on getting home in the early afternoon most days, though.

The first day's a success as James and my mother survive and I manage to attend the Board of Studies meeting from 2–4 pm before heading home. I've finished analysing a set of data one of my undergraduate project students generated earlier in the year and am writing the work up for publication. The results strengthen the case for the electrospray spectrometer I'm building and will be useful if I have to resubmit my grant application.

Tuesday 16 July

Julie started work yesterday and we spent most of the day doing induction stuff. This afternoon I have time on the departmental electrospray mass spectrometer facility to run some test experiments to determine if the work I want Julie to do over the summer will have a chance of succeeding. Feel quite nervous about it because there is so much at stake, but also excited. We've spent the morning being 'proper' chemists, mixing up solutions at the bench. Some of the chemicals were tough to dissolve and we only just got the solutions ready in time. I end up having to skip lunch and go straight on the spectrometer with a loudly protesting stomach. Both sets of experiments work really well though, and when this happens the adrenalin rush saves you from having to eat.

Wednesday 17 July

The EPSRC prioritisation panel meeting is being held today. I had told myself not to expect the proposal to be funded, but as the meeting date has drawn closer I have begun to hope.

Thursday 18 July

Email the administrator who's monitoring my grant application at EPSRC to see if I can get any information about how my proposal has fared. She replies to my email saying that they won't have any news until the middle of next week.

Friday 19 July

Day off work today to attend Jonathan's passing out parade in Grantham. Of course, James doesn't recognise Jonathan in his uniform (I hardly recognise Jonathan in his uniform) but he seems to enjoy the marching and the military band music. After the parade we retire for drinks in the base's pub. James won't look at Jonathan at first but once I encourage him to smack Daddy for going away he seems to cheer up immediately. It may take me a bit longer to get used to Jonathan's brutal new haircut though.

Tuesday 23 July

Can't wait any longer to find out about my grant so I call the programme manager at EPSRC directly. She tells me the proposal isn't going to be funded and has no feedback as to why. It's always disappointing not to get funded but I feel particularly bad this time. I thought it was a sound proposal that deserved support. I'm so excited about the research that I don't want to do anything else. At least I still have some funds from the Royal Society so I'll be able to carry on some work on the project. One of the infuriating things is that I know for sure that several other research groups in the States and Germany already have money to pursue similar projects. Although there's a possibility that my grant may get funded next time, I'll have to wait at least six months, which is a very long time in science. It makes me want to give up altogether.

Friday 26 July

I'm still licking my wounds over my rejected proposal. I tell myself that I should just concentrate on building the funded photodetachment spectrometer for now but it's hard to be sensible when you're sulking. We roll the old laser trolleys out of storage this afternoon as our new lab is finally finished. The trolleys will now enter a new life, as the supports for the photodetachment instrument, and I guess that today therefore marks the beginning of physical work on that project. In a week or so I'm hoping to have the husk of the apparatus in place with the vacuum systems, pumps and pressure gauges. Then we can get on with sorting out the valve and the electron gun while our machine shop is manufacturing the ion optics, which control the ions' paths within the vacuum chamber.

I'm supposed to be making a poster presentation (where you display an outline of your work without giving a paper) of my computational work for a conference in Nottingham next week. I've limited myself to one working day to make the poster, which is probably pushing it a bit and it's likely I'll end up in the department on Sunday morning finishing it off. I'm looking forward to the conference as it's a bit outside my main area of research and I'm hoping to form some new collaborations with theoreticians. Writing this has motivated me to have another bash at working on the poster before I leave today. Finish it at 8.30 pm and cycle home like mad to try to catch James before he goes to bed. Despite my best efforts he's just gone to sleep when I get in. I hate this. It always makes me feel like a bad mother.

Sunday 28 July
A day off. Take James to the Railway Museum in the morning and then spend the afternoon in the park. A gorgeous July day, the sort we only get in Yorkshire once a year, so we make the most of it. Grants and experiments don't seem so important when you have a lazy day like this.

Monday 29 July
Mad morning of running around trying to finish off all kinds of administrative tasks that I should have done last week. Jonathan has to leave for Keele this afternoon for a lectureship interview in the philosophy department, so I can only work a half-day today. I'll have a late night at work on Tuesday.

Tuesday 30 July
I decide to bring James into the lab to finish off some things before leaving for the conference. This seems a simple enough plan. I have visions of James playing with a jigsaw on the floor of my office or doing some colouring while I work. He's been here briefly before and knows where all the good stuff is, so immediately demands my board markers to colour with. My desk and a few memos get trashed, but this is still not too bad and I manage to finish my emailing. Next, I need to make a transparency to take to the conference, which is a nightmare, as the graphics file I wanted to use is incompatible with the software on my computer. James is already restless. He believes (possibly correctly) that the only useful function of a desk-top computer is in calling up the Thomas the Tank Engine website. I oblige and we play the Magic Mountain Gold-dust Game for five minutes until he's bored. Next he turns his attention to my molecular modelling sets, 'Molecule! Molecule!' he demands. I give them to him, abandon the graphics file and finish typing a memo to fax

while James puts the atoms in his mouth. He knows he has my absolute attention now and atoms and bonds are flying everywhere. Pick him up, carry him to the fax room, and manage to fax the purchase order to the American laser company. I still need the transparency though and will need to venture into the student office and print my file, using the newer software there. I resort to the departmental junk food machine and buy James some Quavers. He's instantly pacified and sits in an office chair while I print the transparency I need. James seems relieved to leave the department. I know how he feels.

Wednesday 31 July, Nottingham
I leave for the conference in Nottingham amidst the usual panic of having nothing to wear. Nottingham feels a long way from home and some of the speakers I wanted to hear have cancelled at the last minute. I ring Jonathan who tells me that he didn't get the job. It's not good being away when something like this happens. It's a disappointment, although it seems he got very close. Spend the evening making new contacts at the poster session. Today has felt like hard work.

Tuesday 6 August, York
Minor triumph as the massive poster frames are finally delivered to the department in a very large taxi. I should have done this a long time ago. The framed posters look great, so all I have to do now is get one of the technical staff to put them up on the walls. It's amazing how things like this can use up your mental energy and concentration.

Still, summers are a great time for doing lots of research without teaching and admin getting in the way. I've spent most of the time working with Julie on the departmental electrospray mass spectrometer, looking at metallic ions. This has been a good way to get some hands-on experience with the technology I'll use in my own electrospray spectrometer. I'm also pleased with our progress on the photodetachment spectrometer as all the major features have now been designed and ordered. We're now slowly working through the design and construction of all the smaller instrumental components.

Thursday 12 September
I get back to York after giving an invited lecture at a five-day conference in Southampton. The presentation went well, and the meeting was good fun socially. I also met up with an experimentalist from Crete whose research group uses detector technology similar to the set-up we'll use in our photodetachment spectrometer. He's invited me to visit his group and run some experiments, which should be excellent experience. I'm feeling very bad about leaving James, as I have to go to another conference in Birmingham next week. I buy him a teddy bear to compensate but he's more interested in showing off the raspberry-blowing expertise he acquired while I was away.

doctor and space physiologist
Kevin Fong

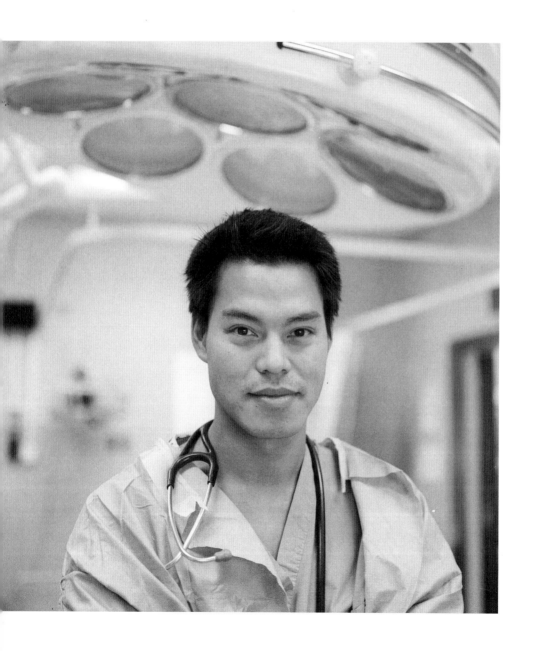

KEVIN FONG is a Senior House Officer in Anaesthetics and Intensive Care in a major city hospital and Honorary Lecturer in Physiology at University College London. He has qualifications in both medicine and astrophysics and, as his diary shows, he is trying to develop an education and research programme for UK space life sciences even while he endeavours to survive as a junior hospital doctor. He is Chairman of the UK Space Biomedical Research and Education Advisory Committee of the British National Space Centre (BNSC) and has worked extensively with the US National Aeronautics and Space Administration (NASA) on medical aspects of the assessment and selection of prospective astronauts and on the medical problems of long-term spaceflight.

His research seeks parallels between the science of astronaut survival and the reaction of the human body to disease or injuries. In 2003, he takes a break from medical practice, using a fellowship from the National Endowment for Science, Technology and the Arts (NESTA) to visit NASA space centers in the USA and investigate extreme-environment physiology. But while compiling his diary, he was still a doctor on call in intensive care, as well as an aspiring space physician.

Friday 21 September 2001, Zero Gravity

I am stuck in the back of a windowless Russian cargo plane which is falling freely out of the Moscow sky. I am wearing a grey, perfectly flammable flight suit, feeling faintly ridiculous and eyeing, with suspicion, the pile of parachutes stowed under the tarpaulin in the corner. NASA would never approve.

All around me the bodies of my fellow passengers are flying wildly out of control about the aircraft and I've just vomited for the second time. The cosmonaut floating opposite me gives me a knowing grin accompanied by a cheery thumbs up. Between retches I return the gesture although somewhat

less energetically. This brief freefall on a parabolic flight is as near as you can get on Earth to the zero gravity experience of an astronaut in orbit. In the world of astronautics this is what passes for 'real fun' and since the age of five I have rarely dreamt of anything else.

Sunday 13 January 2002

Lots to do this weekend even though I'm not on call for Her Majesty's Secret Health Service. In truth the space stuff really started out as a geeky hobby, an in-joke between my friends and me. It used to sit uncomfortably in the background, eclipsed by the demands of my junior medical career. But recently it has become more like a second job.

I have to head up to the Leicester Space Science Centre twice this week, once to give a talk to an industry forum and once to do a television interview. There is also a visit to organise to ESTEC, the European Space Agency's (ESA's) science and technology HQ in Noordwijk in the Netherlands. I'm hoping to take a small research team out there later this month. Until now the UK has had very little to do with human space flight, something I would like to change.

After putting all these things on my task list for the morning, I run down to the shop, buy the fattest Sunday newspaper I can find and read the whole thing slowly from cover to cover before watching the EastEnders omnibus.

Tuesday 15 January

Tired. Have to prepare Thursday's talk in Leicester. Ring Benny Elmann-Larsen, the senior physiology researcher at ESTEC, who now wants to change the meeting date. That is going to cause problems. My juggling act is beginning to look even more precarious than usual. It's going to be a late night.

12.15 am

Still haven't finished that bloody presentation. The temptation to bin the whole thing, go to bed and wing it on the day is huge but that wouldn't be fair to the audience.

2.15 am

Finish at last.

Thursday 17 January

So bloody tired today. My own fault really. Cumulative sleep over the past two nights is probably no more than five hours. Spend the morning watching the surgeons dig bullets out of one of our more unfortunate clients. Finish the afternoon off with a sprint to the station and get to King's Cross just in time to grab the 4.30 to Leicester.

Give the talk to the industry forum. I present some examples of the latest applications derived from space biotechnology. Among these, there are new techniques for growing and engineering human tissues for use in transplant medicine, a mechanical heart designed by a NASA engineer and a cardiothoracic surgeon, a cooling garment used as a therapeutic strategy in multiple sclerosis, and an array of state of the art, non-invasive biosensors. No idea how it goes. The lecture theatre is large and dark with a bright spotlight beaming in my face. Can't see the audience and so can't gauge their reaction. Just as well probably.

Friday 18 January

Later this century the first human will set foot on Martian soil. This mission, if you believe the real rocket scientists, will take up to a thousand days and as much as a year of that time will be spent travelling. So we need to work out how to protect spacemen from the hazards of space flight. Weightlessness can be less fun than it looks and eventually takes its toll on the human body. Astronauts suffer significant muscle and bone loss. Ironically, the best way of simulating this on Earth is to send people to bed. This has spawned a series of somewhat bizarre bed-rest experiments in which healthy volunteers are made to lie down and think of Mars for up to three months. It is the data from one of these experiments that we are hoping to analyse. And this is why I'm desperately trying to rearrange the planned visit to ESTEC. Unfortunately I'm unable to get hold of Hugh Montgomery, the bloke who runs the UCL research team. I'm still trying to juggle appointments in order to secure another meeting with Professor Felsenberg, a bone researcher with the German space agency who is also working on the bed-rest data.

Sunday 20 January

Do a shift in A+E: sore throat – victim of assault – intravenous drug abuser with groin abscess – ruptured cruciate ligament – avulsion fracture of the fifth metatarsal head – common cold – sore throat – cancer of the pancreas – epileptic seizure – common cold – diarrhoea and vomiting – nose bleed – sore throat – child with possible intussusception – foreign body in eye – back pain – common cold – possible appendicitis. Busy. Unsatisfactory. Get home. Exhausted. A few rapid-fire emails. In bed by 1 am. Up again at 6 am.

Monday 21 January

Early start. Out of the door by 6.45 am and a short sprint to Brixton Tube Station. I quite like travelling at this time. At the very least it guarantees you a seat.

A relatively uneventful morning's list in the operating theatres leaves me free to get away on time and head up to the Leicester Space Science Centre to do a bit of filming. It's for a BBC digital channel programme I think. It's good fun, if only to watch the mechanics of television production. Lights, camera, action, all quite exciting really, only partly spoilt by the fact that I ultimately have to talk and look ridiculous on national television. I get back to London at about 10 pm. There is barely enough time left to prepare for my two-day visit to Holland. It's a busy itinerary. On the first day I'll be taking two researchers out to meet Benny Elmann-Larsen. On day two I'll be joined by my collaborator Mike Grocott to get him acquainted with life in the international space programme. The two researchers are Hugh Montgomery and Laurence James (Sid to his mates). Montgomery's lab at UCL is looking at the influence of genetics in osteoporosis, an area of key interest to the space programme. Benny is the head of ESA's physiology programme. Hugh's team have come across a gene that appears to determine how quickly minerals leach out from your bones during periods of inactivity.

Tuesday 22 January, Noordwijk, The Netherlands

Catch an 11 am flight to Amsterdam from London Gatwick with Hugh and Sid in tow. I look forward to visiting ESA centres because they have a different culture from their American and Russian counterparts. NASA is now a federally managed, civilian operation but an unmistakeable thread of the one-time paramilitary outfit still runs through the organisation. For the Russians space is still very much a military concern. Star City, outside Moscow, looks and feels like a military airbase. These days, however, the Russian Space Agency combines this war-like façade uneasily with the capitalist reforms of its parent nation. ESA, unlike its sibs, emerged without the Cold War as a godparent and hence has an atmosphere that goes some small way towards the Utopian sci-fi fantasy of peaceful pan-international space partnership.

Meetings with Benny go well. A meaningful collaboration may yet be built. The day ends gently with a tour of the facilities. There are models of deep-space probes, galleries of astronaut legends and a full-size mock-up of the international space station, but ultimately Hugh and Sid are most impressed with the standard-issue ESA espresso machine in Benny's office.

Wednesday 23 January

Mike arrives painfully early. We spend the morning looking at a web-based, distance learning tool that ESA are using. This basically allows you to give an all-singing, all-dancing, multimedia lecture live from anywhere to anywhere in the world over the Internet. We're hoping to use it as a way round having to fly our ESA and NASA speakers over to lecture on our undergraduate course.

Tuesday 5 February, London

The surgeons take an 80-year-old to theatre to repair a fractured hip. There are some octogenarians who are in remarkable physical condition despite their age. She unfortunately is not among them. Her failing heart and lungs make her a poor candidate for surgery. The anaesthetic alone may kill her but without the surgery her prognosis is extremely poor. If all goes according to plan, much of an anaesthetist's day is taken up with routine surgical lists and anaesthetics that have smooth take-offs, steady flights and soft landings. When it goes wrong it goes wrong quickly and profoundly. Fixing the problems demands a real-time, working knowledge of pharmacology, physiology, medicine, surgery and physics, as well as steady nerves. This time, all is well. So far.

Wednesday 6 February

I can tell from the moment we arrive that the impossibly blue-skinned man lying dead on the bed is going to stay that way. This, almost invariably, is the outcome of a cardiac arrest on the wards. We leave. I ritually wash my hands and go home without giving it a further thought.

It wasn't always like that. As a medical student every crash call, every death was a major event. I remember the first time I saw a cardiac arrest. I was in the resuscitation room wearing a short white coat with a brand new stethoscope around my neck. It was messy and noisy and sad. At the end the woman lay there with the clothes shorn unceremoniously from her body, oozing blood from the needle puncture sites, blue, cold and alone. It was my first death. I remember being determined to record the event accurately, recognising it in some way as a rite of passage. By the end of the shift I couldn't even remember her name. And then you qualify and eventually you see so many that it doesn't even register. I used to wonder if that might be a bad thing. Now I don't even wonder about that.

Thursday and Friday 7–8 February

Start my first day on the Intensive Care Unit (ICU) at 8.30 am.

A 27-hour stretch ahead of me. The unit itself is calm at the moment. My patients include a man recovering from surgery to repair a ruptured abdominal aortic aneurysm. This, in lay terms, is basically what happens if the biggest artery in your body bursts. By the numbers his prognosis is appalling. Ninety per cent of these patients die, and this man might yet do so, but at least for now he's looking pretty good.

I get to bed at midnight. My room is only a few hundred feet from the unit, on the edge of one of the main thoroughfares in the hospital. It is difficult to get to sleep there at the best of times. I am woken at around 2 am by the ICU nurses who want to talk about a woman whose haemoglobin is falling. I walk down to the unit, see the patient (who looks perfectly OK), read the notes, examine her, repeat the tests and go back to sleep. I'm woken again at 3.03 am. The new test results are even worse. According to the numbers the patient is bleeding to death. I head back to the unit to see the patient again. She is comfortable, well and all of her vital signs are stable. This still doesn't add up particularly well. I send a third set of tests, this time to the main laboratories for a more accurate assessment. I sit around waiting for the blood samples to be processed and by 4.10 am I have a result: all is well. Back to bed, perchance to sleep. No such luck. Up again at 6.45 am for more of the same and this time I don't get back to my room again. I hand over to the incoming senior house officer at 8.30 am and, after a painful ward round, finish at 10.30 am.

Haven't done an all-night marathon for a while and am suffering for it. I could sleep on my feet. I catch the train home, fall asleep and wake up at Old Street, which is three stations past my stop. I work a 1 in 4 on-call rota which means that, on average, I am on call every fourth day. The next 24-hour stint is Monday.

Get home and try to keep going. Things to do: mark the essays written by the students from the Space and Extreme Environment Physiology course that I run at UCL, set the exam, and circulate the overdue minutes from last December's UK Space Biomedical Research and Education Advisory Committee meeting.

Monday 11 February

Back on call again. The ICU is busy.

Sunday 17 February

It happens so quickly I barely have time to react. One minute the patient in bed 5 is awake, alert and seemingly stable, the next he is collapsed in a heap with a fully obstructed airway, leaving him unable to breathe and us unable to ventilate him.

We attempt to insert a tube into his windpipe but there is too much swelling around his larynx – the airway is completely blocked. We clamp a rubber mask to his face. The mask is attached to a bag which we squeeze in an effort to push oxygen into his lungs. Every artificial breath leaks hopelessly out of his mouth, spilling under the rubber seal. His rosy, well-oxygenated appearance gives way to thundercloud grey in seconds. He is suffocating. Only a single option remains. I take a scalpel and begin to cut his throat. The surgical team and my boss have been called. For the moment, though it is just us. There is at this point the distant recollection of an anatomy lesson. This is an emergency tracheotomy. It is the stuff of urban legend amongst medical students – the story of a man in a restaurant, choking to death on a lump of gristle that is firmly lodged in his throat, whose life is saved by having a Bic biro stabbed through his throat by a gung-ho, bionic junior doctor. The idea is that you bypass the blockage to the windpipe and blow oxygen in through the hole that you've made.

If only it were so simple. After cutting through the thin layer of skin and fat I am unable to locate the trachea. It isn't where it should be. Futile fumbling from me. There is a probe clipped to his finger that monitors the oxygen saturation of his blood with every pulse. Things have generally gone pretty badly wrong if you get down to the 80 per cent area. His oxygen saturation is currently 30 per cent and I still can't find the trachea. Did I make the incision in the wrong place? Is the incision too shallow? Am I too far to the left? To the right?

Just as things begin to look truly hopeless, as I stand over him fishing uselessly around in the hole in his neck, the surgeon and consultant anaesthetist burst through the door and, between them, manage to finish the job and save his life.

Tuesday 19 February

The man in bed 5 is sitting up, breathing through his own mouth, and using his own lungs without any help from us. He is well enough to smile and wave at me. The only sign of his weekend ordeal is an untidy scar across his throat held together by a neat row of stitches.

Wednesday 20 February

I finally return the second draft of the exam paper for the undergraduate course. There is still the spectre of overdue marking to tackle and those minutes to circulate. Need to prepare for another meeting with the Medical Research Council (MRC) and British National Space Centre (BNSC) teams on Friday to talk about organising workshops for space physiology.

Friday 22 February

The MRC workshops on space physiology are to go ahead. This is exactly what we have been pushing for over the last four years. It's going to involve a lot of work.

Thursday 14 March

Spend the morning at a meeting of the Life and Physical Sciences Network Group at the BNSC. It meets quarterly to discuss the state of the space programme in the UK, or at least what passes for a space programme. We talk about possible futures, attempt to tease out the important scientific questions to which space exploration might hold the key and try to find a way forward.

There are two sides to the science of astronaut survival. We want to know how to protect crews from the extremes presented by long-duration space flight, an obstacle that needs to be surmounted before Martian expeditions can work. But human studies in this environment have the potential to yield new and unique insight into mechanisms underlying fundamental physiological and biological processes. The astronauts' goal, like that of all seasoned travellers, is to return safe and well at the end of their journey having gained a better understanding of themselves along the way.

We spend a fair proportion of the meeting dizzying ourselves with the truly exciting possibilities that the wider international space programme has to offer before grounding ourselves in the harsh realities of the UK position. The personalities around the table range from ardent proponents to the utterly ambivalent. It makes for a lively exchange at times.

Friday and Saturday 15–16 March

At the ICU, on call. Tough day at work. Three drawn-out cardiac arrests, two brutally honest discussions, four relatives in tears, one death amongst the patients on the ICU, one critically ill bloke who needs to be scooped off the wards and transferred to the newly vacant bed in ICU. Elsewhere my physiology students at UCL are hassling me for not having marked their coursework essays, which are now well overdue. I get home late on Saturday morning and catch some sleep ready to go back to another on-call stretch tomorrow morning.

Wednesday 20 March
Up late trying to build a case for BNSC to fund a fact-finding trip to Houston. Look over some review material about artificial gravity habitats – we're probably going to need it if we're ever going to send people to Mars.

Tuesday and Wednesday 26–27 March
On call. Work pretty much straight through from 8 am until 1 am the next day. Head back to Central London on Wednesday morning. Meet with my MRC and BNSC colleagues at 10 am to discuss the developing plans for the forthcoming space physiology workshop. There is plenty to do. It looks as if I'll be off to Houston in May to prepare NASA for their role in the workshop. Back to the research office at UCL. Add the final touches to a revision lecture on space physiology for my students and give it at midday. The class sit there expectantly, waiting for me to hint at the content of the final exam and I, in turn, delight in disappointing them.

Wednesday 10 April
Play email tennis with BNSC. Trying to set up our visit to Houston. Manage to finalise an abstract for submission to the ESA's Life Sciences Symposium. Join up the dots with the bone team.

Thursday and Friday 18–19 April
On call for intensive care. Start work at 8.30 am with seven patients. Two of these are so sick that by 11 am I have only five left.

Monday 22 April 2002
Tough week ahead. Will spend every other night on call and will work over 100 hours before next Monday morning. On weeks like this you just hold your breath, take the plunge and wait until you get out the other side.

Thursday and Friday 25–26 April
Second 24-hour on-call shift in the last three days. ICU is almost empty for a

change. Use the rare down-time to ring ESA and chase up the collaboration that Hugh, Sid and I kicked off in Amsterdam.

Tuesday and Wednesday 30 April–1 May
On call for the fifth time in nine days. Quiet today. Thankfully. Sleep for seven continuous hours. I'm well rested enough to head into town and catch a series of lectures about diving and aviation medicine at the Association of Anaesthetists.

Saturday 4 May
Struggle out of bed. In spite of my fatigued state last night, I unwisely decided to add insult to injury with alcohol and curry. Doing the first day of my PADI diving course this morning. Get to the class late and try to turn my brain over to theory.

I spend the afternoon at the bottom of a small pool in Bayswater breathing compressed air. Even in this tiny expanse of water sub-aqua life appears wonderfully serene. So much so that I am temporarily distracted from my hungover state. It is interesting. At least I find it interesting, that the human physiological envelope is so narrow but that we as individuals are capable of exhibiting such resilience at its edges. A few dozen metres below the surface of the ocean and the air we breathe rapidly becomes toxic. And yet we exist here, more than exist, we dive here for fun, cheating the physics and stretching our physiology with exotic gas mixtures, pushing at the boundary and hoping that it won't push back.

Balanced on another edge, a few thousand metres above, on the roof of the world, where there is barely enough pressure to push molecules of oxygen across the thin lining of our lungs into our bloodstream, where all the energy we can muster is just enough to keep us breathing, a bold few somehow manage to find the will to climb mountains.

Intensive Care is much the same. We push, we cheat and we wait for the patients to find the will. It's just another edge.

Friday and Saturday 10–11 May
On call for ICU. Sometime after midday a strange thing happens. Every pager in the hospital goes off at the same time. I have heard this chorus only once before in my career and my Pavlovian response brings me out in a cold sweat. 'Major Incident Declared' squawks my pager. It is the Potters Bar rail crash.

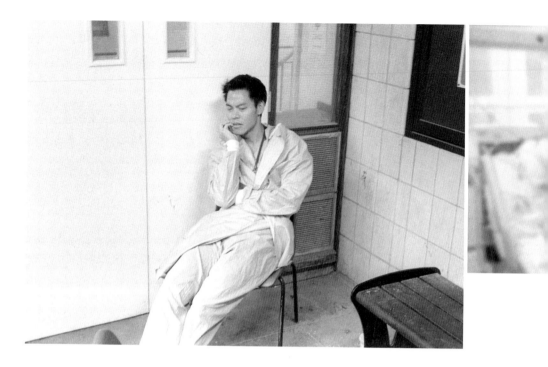

Every hospital has, or should have, a well-rehearsed plan for such eventualities. It is all that prevents these situations from turning into total catastrophe.

Bewilderment and confusion are the first responses, followed by the slow realisation that your routine day at work has just evaporated. I am sent to the Accident and Emergency Department to report and be assigned a role. By the time I arrive the London Ambulance Service is calling for a mobile team to go out to the scene. There are few justifications for making such a request. The only two that I can immediately think of are overwhelming casualty numbers and multiple people trapped at the scene. Both scenarios can only make you shudder. The team is to comprise three doctors and three intensive care and theatre nurses. We head to the stores to draw our kit. We wait.

Eventually the team is stood down. There is a sense of relief. We disrobe, return our kit to the stores and are assigned new roles in the resuscitation rooms in A+E. In all there are seven dead and 76 injured.

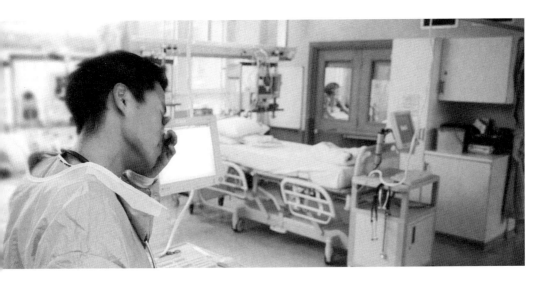

Monday 13 May
Health Secretary Alan Milburn and Prince Charles visit, though not at the same time. The floors gleam, the windows sparkle and, for the first time in two years, the roof covering the entrance to the ICU doesn't leak.

Sunday 19 May
Here I stand at the water's edge, stuffed uncomfortably into an ill-fitting neoprene wetsuit, mask and snorkel pinching my face, barely able to breathe. At my instructor's command I plunge into the freezing Portsmouth water and gulp air from my regulator. I'm finally learning to dive. Our class bobs around in a tight cluster on the surface for a few minutes before dropping below the chop and descending all of six metres to the bottom of the reservoir. There are half a dozen of us and most, including me, get our buoyancy all wrong. We thud into the silt like lead and throw up so much crap that in seconds I have lost the rest of my class. When the clouds clear the instructor tows me around the wreck of a small sunken boat. We swim in circles around it, peering into portholes. This is the diving equivalent of learning to ride a bike starting on a tricycle with stabilisers.

Monday 20 May, National Aeronautics and Space Administration, Lyndon B. Johnson Space Center, Houston, Texas
I return today to the city where my adventures in the space programme began.

This is Johnson Space Center, home of NASA's astronaut training ground. In the past I have worked here with the medical operations group comparing the physiology of ageing and space flight, addressing some of the medical issues relevant to astronaut selection and discussing the capabilities required for an emergency crew return vehicle.

I am here in a quasi-political role as part of a UK delegation whose aim is to explore possibilities with NASA. For the first time in many years we are beginning to edge our way back into the space programme proper. The UK has been shut out of this effort for so long that it will take some years before it can rehabilitate itself and be reintegrated into the space community. This is perhaps part of the beginning of that process. I am uncertain of what this visit will bring or where the story will finally end but I live, as always, in hope.

Tuesday 21 May

The weather is uncharacteristically fine for this time of year and we manage to escape the humid Houston soup, enjoying instead sunshine and dry warmth. Everything in Houston happens on a truly American scale. The skyline dominated by towering, mirrored pillars, the highways choked with oversized trucks driven by oversized Texans; it is a natural home for the space center.

Meet with the British Consulate in the morning to go through the itinerary. The schedule is busy. The one minor, positive side effect of living a life of interrupted sleep patterns is that jet lag loses its bite. The day after a ten-hour transatlantic flight spanning five time zones you feel much the same as you do on any other day. Things have changed here since last September. I was last at Johnson Space Center at the start of 2001. At that time, with my paper badge, I could drive on and off the facility without hindrance. But the new threat has brought with it new paranoia. We leave our cars at the gate and are escorted every step of the way by NASA officials.

Friday 24 May

Visit Spacehab this morning, a commercial organisation who will put a payload into orbit for you if you chuck them a half million dollars or so. Their offices are up near Ellington Field on a nondescript piece of land at a nondescript crossroads just outside Clearlake. T38 jet aircraft, in which pilot astronauts earn their spurs, blast off and head out over the Gulf of Mexico. We finish the meeting. The Spacehab representative's parting shot is: 'If there's anything we can do to get you guys into space then let us know.' If only.

Hugo Glendinning

HUGO GLENDINNING has a reputation as an outstanding arts photographer and works regularly for dance and theatre companies, including the National Theatre, the Royal Ballet, Royal Shakespeare Company and Rambert Dance Company, as well as West End production and international ballet companies.

Contemporary dance is one of his great passions and over the past ten years he has developed a close working relationship with many choreographers and dancers. In the field of experimental theatre Hugo has a unique collaborative practice with Forced Entertainment Theatre Cooperative. He has worked with writer/director Tim Etchells in different media, including documentary film (*DIY* for Channel 4 TV), CD ROM (*Nightwalks, Frozen Palaces, Spin*), video production (*Filthy Words and Phrases*) and installation pieces for art galleries (*Rules of the Game, Ground Plans for Paradise, Red Room*).

Hugo has been commissioned by most of the major magazines and newspapers in Britain and by many in Europe and America. His two major advertising contracts in the past couple of years have been for Guinness (Brann Advertising) and Teletubbies (Ragdoll Productions).

His photographs for *Art, not Chance: Nine artists' diaries* were highly praised.

Also published by the Calouste Gulbenkian Foundation

Art, not Chance: Nine artists' diaries

Edited by Paul Allen
Photographs by Hugo Glendinning

Bobby Baker, Shobana Jeyasingh, Joanna MacGregor, Lawrence Norfolk, Jo Shapcott, Shelagh Stephenson, Tim Supple, Errollyn Wallen, Richard Wentworth.

Nine artists, successful in different branches of the arts, each kept a diary over a period of a few months reflecting on their work in progress. The resulting narratives make an absorbing read and powerfully illuminate the process of making art. Music is improvised and composed, new artworks conceived and displayed or performed, a novel is completed, poems are written, new plays evolve and old plays are reinterpreted. The diaries offer glimpses into the authors' personal and professional lives and though each is distinctively different, all reveal that art is made in a practical matter-of-fact way.

'... surprisingly intimate access to the agonies and ecstasies of creative minds ... it made me want to read the novel, hear the music, see the show.' Robert Hewison, *The Guardian*

'... a riveting reminder that the business of artists is the making of art ... an absorbing and often humorous book ... jump at it.' Lisa Apignanesi, *The Independent*

£8.50 pbk ISBN 0 903319 94 2 (2001)

Strange and Charmed: Science and the contemporary visual arts

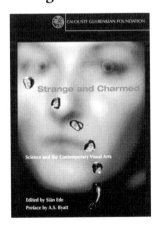

Edited by Siân Ede
Preface by A.S. Byatt

Strange and Charmed is the first book to investigate the burgeoning fascination of contemporary visual artists with science. With a preface by A.S. Byatt and contributions by distinguished art historian Martin Kemp, artist Andrea Duncan, Wellcome Trust Head of Exhibitions Ken Arnold, artist/physicist Richard Bright and cognitive psychologist Mike Page, the book identifies a new relationship between art and science and looks at its implications for both cultures. Many adventurous works are discussed and illustrated, including Helen Chadwick's sensitive creations involving human embryos, James Acord's radioactive sculptures, Kitsou Dubois's award-winning choreography in zero gravity, and Cornelia Parker's *Cold Dark Matter*, and the new work beginning to emerge from artist/scientist collaborations.

'We need to feel there is some-thing real out there – of which we are a part and not the whole – and science reveals it to us.' A.S. Byatt

£10.99 pbk ISBN 0 903319 87 X (2000)

Available from Central Books, 99 Wallis Road, London E9 5LN
Tel: 0845 458 9911, Fax: 0845 458 9912, Email: orders@centralbooks.com
Website: www.centralbooks.co.uk